# INSTRUCTOR'S QUIZ BOOK

# THE PRENTICE HALL READER

## EIGHTH EDITION

### GEORGE MILLER
*University of Delaware*

PEARSON

Prentice
Hall

Upper Saddle River, New Jersey 07458

© 2007 by PEARSON EDUCATION, INC.
Upper Saddle River, New Jersey 07458

ISBN 0-13-195574-8

Printed in the United States of America

# CONTENTS

# PREFACE

These Content and Vocabulary Quizzes are intended to be administered and graded quickly. They provide the instructor with a brief and efficient means of testing the student's ability to extract significant ideas from the readings and of demonstrating his or her understanding of certain vocabulary words as they are used in the essays.

Questions on content are primarily factual, requiring little judgment on the part of the student--except for a few questions that involve an understanding of the method of development being used.

Vocabulary words have been selected, in large part, for the purpose of broadening the student's vocabulary while, at the same time, clarifying the meanings of words necessary to the understanding of the particular selection.

Questions and/or comments on rhetoric and style are provided in the questions that follow each selection in the *Reader*, insuring that the more sophisticated aspects of comprehension, interpretation, and application to the students' writings are covered.

Keys to both Content and Vocabulary Quizzes are included at the back of this Quiz Book.

This revision of the Quiz Book incorporates material prepared for the first edition by Janet Eber, for the second by Henrietta Twining, for the fifth by Mark Gallaher, and for the eighth by Eric Miller.

George Miller

# CHAPTER 1: CONTENT QUIZ

## Anna Quindlen, "The Name is Mine"

NAME _____          DATE

1. At the beginning of the essay, Quindlen responds to the name "Mrs. Krovatin" because

    a. that is the name by which she identifies herself.
    b. she is upset and not paying attention.
    c. it identifies her as a family member.

2. The event that triggers her response to that name is that

    a. her husband has been injured in an accident.
    b. her son has been injured in an accident.
    c. a doctor calls her on the telephone.

3. Quindlen didn't take her husband's last name because

    a. she didn't want to lose her own identity.
    b. she didn't like her husband's last name.
    c. she feels that a woman should never take her husband's name.

4. The image that she uses to symbolize what taking her husband's name would be like is

    a. joining hands in wedlock.
    b. hiding beneath the umbrella of her husband's identity.
    c. forging ties that bind.

5. The consequence of Quindlen's decision to keep her own name is that

    a. she must explain to people who she is.
    b. she is the only member of her family with a different name.
    c. she regrets her original decision.

# CHAPTER 1: VOCABULARY QUIZ

Anna Quindlen, "The Name is Mine"

NAME _____     DATE

Directions: Choose the correct definition for each of the following words.

1. ADJUNCT

    a. a partner
    b. someone who stands beside
    c. a subordinate or helper

2. DISINGENUOUSLY

    a. stupidly
    b. insincerely
    c. distractingly

3. EXHILARATING

    a. exciting or stimulating
    b. tiring
    c. boring

4. HYPHENATED

    a. of Greek origins
    b. separated by a hyphen (-)
    c. made up or invented

5. DISDAINFUL

    a. scornful
    b. proud
    c. hateful

# CHAPTER 1: CONTENT QUIZ

## Bob Greene, "Cut"

NAME _____          DATE

1. In this essay, Greene relates the stories of five men, each of which is told in

    a. first person.
    b. second person.
    c. third person.

2. These five examples support Greene's contention that

    a. being "cut from the team" is a traumatic experience.
    b. being "cut from the team" is embarrassing.
    c. being "cut from the team" may make one a super-achiever later in life.
    d. all of the above

3. Each of these five men relates how the experience of "being cut"

    a. affected his choice of career.
    b. had a profound effect upon his life in general.
    c. affected his attitude toward sports.

4. All the experiences occurred when these men were

    a. in junior high or high school.
    b. in college.
    c. in elementary school.

5. The devastating "message" that each young man received from the experience was

    a. "You're not good enough."
    b. "You'll never be a successful executive."
    c. "Better luck next time!"

# CHAPTER 1: VOCABULARY QUIZ

### Bob Greene, "Cut"

NAME _____     DATE

Directions: Choose the correct definition for each of the following words.

1. INORDINATELY

    a. carefully
    b. supportively
    c. excessively

2. PERCEPTION

    a. understanding
    b. success
    c. disappointment

3. SELF-ESTEEM

    a. one's attitude toward an individual
    b. favorable impression of oneself
    c. preoccupation with oneself

4. ARTICULATE

    a. to speak with an accent
    b. to express clearly and distinctly
    c. to stand at attention

5. STOIC

    a. without emotion
    b. with respect
    c. without understanding

Edwidge Danticat, "Westbury Court"

NAME _____          DATE

1. What is "Westbury Court"?

    a. the name of the town in which the narrator grew up
    b. the name of the housing development in which the narrator lived as a child
    c. the name of the apartment building in which the narrator lived when she was fourteen

2. What was the narrator doing when the fire broke out?

    a. watching *General Hospital* on television
    b. playing outside with her younger brothers
    c. sleeping

3. Who were the Parent Brothers?

    a. the two boys who died in the fire
    b. a Haitian musical group who lived in Westbury Court
    c. the narrator's favorite rap group

4. In thinking about the tragedy, what "lesson" does the narrator draw from the experience?

    a. that children should never be left alone, without an adult present
    b. that playing with matches is dangerous
    c. that Westbury Court is a dangerous place to live
    d. that the real world is not safe

5. Who in the essay says, "Sometimes it is too late to say, 'I shouldn't have.'"?

    a. the narrator
    b. the mother of the two children who die in the fire
    c. the narrator's mother in reference to the fire

# CHAPTER 1: VOCABULARY QUIZ

## Edwidge Danticat, "Westbury Court"

NAME _____     DATE

Directions: Choose the correct definition for each of the following words.

1. BURLY

    a. hairy
    b. big and strong
    c. angry

2. ESCORTED

    a. made friends with; befriended
    b. cut short
    c. went with; accompanied

3. SINGED

    a. completed
    b. praised
    c. slightly burned

4. INADVERTENTLY

    a. unintentionally; without meaning to
    b. intentionally; planned
    c. casually; informally

5. REMINISCE

    a. to remember
    b. to dispose of
    c. to lessen; to make smaller

# CHAPTER 1: CONTENT QUIZ

George Orwell, "On Shooting an Elephant"

NAME _____          DATE

1. What was it that the old woman did not want the children to see?

    a. the angry elephant
    b. the body of the dead man
    c. the shooting of the elephant

2. What does Orwell say about information in the East?

    a. It travels fast.
    b. It is always reliable.
    c. It becomes less clear the closer you get to it.

3. To what does Orwell compare shooting a working elephant?

    a. stealing from a shopkeeper
    b. digging up a corpse
    c. destroying a piece of machinery
    d. none of the above

4. According to Orwell, what happens when the white man turns tyrant?

    a. He destroys his own freedom.
    b. He becomes damned to hell.
    c. He will overcome all obstacles.

5. How long does it take for the elephant to die?

    a. He dies instantaneously.
    b. about two hours
    c. thirty minutes
    d. one day

# CHAPTER 1: VOCABULARY QUIZ

George Orwell, "On Shooting an Elephant"

NAME _____     DATE

Directions: Choose the correct definition for each of the following words.

1. PRETEXT

    a. an excuse for doing something
    b. a desire
    c. an inclination

2. SENILITY

    a. physical illness
    b. youthfulness
    c. infirmity

3. INNUMERABLE

    a. horrible; frightening
    b. countless
    c. difficult

4. FUTILITY

    a. practicality
    b. flexibility
    c. pointlessness

5. SQUALID

    a. filthy
    b. empty
    c. uncivilized or primitive

# CHAPTER 1: CONTENT QUIZ

Leslie Heywood, "One of the Girls"

NAME _____          DATE

1. Gertrude Ederle was

    a. the first woman to run the Boston Marathon.
    b. the first woman to win Wimbledon.
    c. the first woman to swim the English Channel.

2. Title IX of the Education Act of 1972 prohibited discrimination on the basis of

    a. race.
    b. national origin.
    c. gender.
    d. physical capabilities.

3. According to Heywood, the "female athlete triad" includes

    a. swimming, running, and gymnastics.
    b. eating disorders, exercise compulsion, and amenorrhea.
    c. high school, college, and professional competitions.

4. For Heywood, sports offer young women the possibility to

    a. stay thin and attractive.
    b. become popular among their peers.
    c. develop a sense of competence and power.

5. In writing about her own career as a competitive runner, Heywood remembers

    a. the good times that she had as a member of a team.
    b. the sense of a self-destructive competitiveness.
    c. the physical exhilaration that came with intense physical exercise.

# CHAPTER 1: VOCABULARY QUIZ

Leslie Heywood, "One of the Girls"

NAME _____     DATE

Directions: Choose the correct definition for each of the following words.

1. PRECEDED

    a. came before
    b. came after
    c. came at the same time

2. TRIAD

    a. a group of three
    b. any competitive event
    c. a track and field competition

3. DISPARAGED

    a. criticized; belittled
    b. praised
    c. encouraged

4. INTERSCHOLASTIC

    a. within a particular school
    b. among other schools
    c. not connected with schools; detached from schools

5. INSTINCTIVELY

    a. artificially
    b. quietly
    c. naturally

# CHAPTER 2: CONTENT QUIZ

Langston Hughes, "Salvation"

NAME _____          DATE

1. Hughes relates a significant personal experience that occurred when he was

    a. a small child.
    b. twelve-going-on-thirteen.
    c. a college-age young adult.

2. Because of what Hughes' Auntie Reed has told him about what will happen when he is saved,

    a. he is frightened and does not want to attend the special revival meeting for youth.
    b. he enjoys participating with the others on the mourners' bench.
    c. he lingers on the mourners' bench, confused because he expects to see Jesus.

3. Hughes's companion Westley approaches the altar because

    a. he decides he truly wants to be saved.
    b. he is tired of sitting on the bench.
    c. he wants to do what will make his father happy.

4. Hughes cries at home in bed that night because

    a. he is so happy that the Holy Ghost has come into his life.
    b. he is disappointed and remorseful because he feels he has deceived his aunt and the other church members.
    c. he is lonely and misses his parents and friends back home.

5. As a result of this experience, Hughes

    a. dedicates his life to becoming a minister.
    b. no longer believes there is a Jesus anymore.
    c. fears God will strike him dead because of his behavior that night and refuses to return to the revival meeting.

# CHAPTER 2: VOCABULARY QUIZ

## Langston Hughes, "Salvation"

NAME _____ DATE

Directions: Choose the correct definition for each of the following words.

1. DIRE

      a. vivid
      b. make-believe
      c. dreadful

2. GNARLED

      a. twisted
      b. disciplined
      c. pointed

3. SERENELY

      a. peacefully
      b. boisterously or loudly
      c. emotionally

4. PUNCTUATED

      a. filled with
      b. broken or interrupted by
      c. commented on

5. ECSTATIC

      a. barely audible
      b. sorrowful
      c. overwhelmingly joyful

# CHAPTER 2: CONTENT QUIZ

## Maya Angelou, "Sister Monroe"

NAME _____     DATE

1. Since the episode of "Sister Monroe" is an autobiographical narrative, it is told from what point of view?

     a. first person
     b. second person
     c. third person

2. Angelou describes a Sunday morning in church when Sister Monroe

     a. fainted from the heat.
     b. "got the spirit."
     c. led the congregation in a special prayer.

3. According to the author, Sister Monroe made up for her frequent absences from church by

     a. holding Bible study classes in her home.
     b. shouting loudly when she did attend.
     c. ministering to the needy.

4. As Sister Monroe engages in her usual activity at church,

     a. others join in.
     b. the children laugh.
     c. everyone sits quietly and stares.

5. Angelou reports that the minister, Reverend Thomas,

     a. becomes distracted and quits preaching.
     b. demands that order be restored immediately.
     c. is undaunted and continues to the end of the service.

# CHAPTER 2: VOCABULARY QUIZ

## Maya Angelou, "Sister Monroe"

NAME _____ DATE

Directions: Choose the correct definition for each of the following words.

1. OMINOUS

   a. threatening
   b. powerful
   c. sacred

2. ORDAINED

   a. suggested
   b. ordered
   c. mentioned

3. LOATHING

   a. enjoying
   b. detesting
   c. fearing

4. PANDEMONIUM

   a. peace and quiet
   b. wild disorder
   c. spirit of joy

5. INFUSED

   a. dismissed
   b. annoyed
   c. inspired

CHAPTER 2: CONTENT QUIZ


Tom Haines, "Facing Famine"


NAME _____          DATE


1. What does Gebi say the land makes you want to do?

    a. sleep
    b. eat
    c. escape
    d. die

2. What piece of equipment was left stuck in the dry ground?

    a. a shovel
    b. an empty water bucket
    c. a broken drill bit

3. How long has it been since the last time that it rained?

    a. two weeks
    b. one year
    c. six months

4. Which of the following is NOT one of the words Berhanu agrees to feeling?

    a. anger
    b. hate
    c. terror

5. On what continent is the famine occurring?

    a. India
    b. Africa
    c. South America

# CHAPTER 2: VOCABULARY QUIZ

Tom Haines, "Facing Famine"

NAME _____          DATE

Directions: Choose the correct definition for each of the following words.

1. MEAGER

    a. simply
    b. scanty
    c. dirty

2. THRIVE

    a. to prosper
    b. to reproduce
    c. to destroy

3. PARCHED

    a. cracked
    b. broken into pieces
    c. dried up

4. EMPATHY

    a. regret
    b. compassion
    c. contempt

5. SAUNTER

    a. to stroll
    b. to walk quickly
    c. to jog

# CHAPTER 2: CONTENT QUIZ

### Judith Ortiz Cofer, "Marina"

NAME _____       DATE

1. Cofer and her mother are often in conflict because

    a. Cofer is ashamed of her mother's lack of education.
    b. Cofer's mother has more traditional ideas than her daughter about what a woman's role should be.
    c. Cofer believes that her mother should live with her in the United States rather than stay in Puerto Rico.

2. In Cofer's grandmother's day, the older girls of the village would gather at a private spot located

    a. near a statue of the Black Virgin.
    b. at the mouth of a mysterious cavern.
    c. alongside a clear stream.

3. All the girls wanted the shy Marina

    a. to become a nun.
    b. to braid their hair.
    c. to sing with her lovely voice.

4. Kiki, who would eventually disappear with Marina, was

    a. the wealthy mayor's daughter.
    b. the poor daughter of a reclusive widow.
    c. the first to have seen the Black Virgin.

5. What significance does the story of Marina and Kiki have for Cofer and her mother?

    a. It is a warning that mothers and daughters must learn to reconcile their differences.
    b. It offers them a new place to begin to define the word woman.
    c. It reminds them that they both were adolescents once, sharing the same hopes and fears.

# CHAPTER 2: VOCABULARY QUIZ

Judith Ortiz Cofer, "Marina"

NAME _____          DATE

Directions:  Choose the correct definition for each of the following words.

1.  VIBRANT

    a. never satisfied
    b. full of life
    c. impolite

2.  SVELTE

    a. slender
    b. sophisticated
    c. magical

3.  BOUDOIR

    a. a type of braided hairstyle
    b. a Spanish-style blouse
    c. an elaborate bedroom or sitting room

4.  IDYLLIC

    a. all alone; completely isolated
    b. characterized by peace and contentment
    c. lazy; unwilling to work

5.  HEIRLOOM

    a. something handed down from generation to generation
    b. an object of great monetary value, such as a gold necklace
    c. a person who has inherited a great estate

CHAPTER 2: CONTENT QUIZ


Evans D. Hopkins, "Lockdown"


NAME _____          DATE


1.  What is a prison "lockdown"?

    a. the use of chains and handcuffs to keep a violent inmate under control
    b. a period during which all inmates are continuously confined to their cells with only
       very restricted movement under guard
    c. the practice of chaining prisoners together by their hands and feet so they can be moved
       from place to place or sent out to a chain gang site

2. Of all the personal items Hopkins could no longer keep in his cell, which did he miss the
   most?

    a. his family photos
    b. his collection of law books
    c. his typewriter

3. What feeling does Hopkins say a prisoner must avoid at all costs to survive prison life?

    a. self-pity
    b. boredom
    c. trust

4. How have prison policies in general changed since Hopkins first entered prison some fifteen
   years before?

    a. Prisoners have more opportunities for rehabilitation and educational programs.
    b. Prisoners have fewer opportunities for rehabilitation and educational programs.
    c. Nothing has really changed.

5. What does Hopkins say he has that many of the younger prisoners do not?

    a. hope of being paroled
    b. an interest in bettering himself
    c. a supportive family

# CHAPTER 2: VOCABULARY QUIZ

Evans D. Hopkins, "Lockdown"

NAME _____     DATE

Directions:  Choose the correct definition for each of the following words.

1.  FEIGNED

    a. pretended
    b. passed out
    c. relating to something foreign

2.  INSOUCIANCE

    a. a kind of dessert
    b. backtalk
    c. lack of worry or concern

3.  DISQUIETING

    a. upsetting; disturbing
    b. making a noise or racket
    c. whispering together

4.  ANATHEMA

    a. a song sung on patriotic occasions
    b. a skin disease that causes redness and scratching
    c. something disliked or to be avoided

5.  UNPRECEDENTED

    a. not easily understood
    b. copied; not original
    c. never having been seen or experienced before

# CHAPTER 3: CONTENT QUIZ

## Debra Anne Davis, "A Pen by the Phone"

NAME _____          DATE

1. What is the point to the story that Davis tells?

    a. how funny her father was
    b. how smart her father was
    c. how she and her sister fought
    d. how oblivious her father could be

2. What was her father's primary hobby?

    a. cooking
    b. watching television
    c. reading

3. What did her father teach Davis?

    a. simplicity
    b. honesty
    c. loyalty
    d. faith

4. How did her father teach her?

    a. by lecturing her
    b. by being an example
    c. by having her practice

5. What does Davis say that her father had few of?

    a. needs
    b. problems
    c. wants

# CHAPTER 3: VOCABULARY QUIZ

### Debra Anne Davis, "A Pen by the Phone"

NAME _____     DATE

Directions: Choose the correct definition for each of the following words.

1. UNBIDDEN

    a. voluntarily
    b. carelessly
    c. quickly

2. PLEA

    a. an ultimatum
    b. a request
    c. a shout

3. AMIDST

    a. close to
    b. surrounded by fog
    c. in the middle of

4. DEVASTATING

    a. pleasing
    b. emptying
    c. overwhelming

5. RECOLLECTION

    a. a daydream
    b. a remembrance
    c. a gathering together

# CHAPTER 3: CONTENT QUIZ

## N. Scott Momaday, "The Way to Rainy Mountain"

NAME _____          DATE

1. Momaday has returned to Rainy Mountain because

    a. he wishes to visit his grandmother's grave.
    b. he is working on a history of his ancestors.
    c. he wishes to visit his grandmother.

2. The Kiowas were originally

    a. mountain people who moved to the Plains.
    b. Plains people who moved to the mountains.
    c. a Southwestern tribe.

3. In the essay, Momaday focuses on

    a. his grandmother and her life.
    b. his grandmother as a representative of the Kiowa nation.
    c. the relationship that exists between the Kiowa and nature.
    d. all of the above.

4. Momaday recounts the legend of the Devil's Tower because

    a. it is where his grandmother is buried.
    b. it is an example of how the Kiowa saw mythic significance in nature.
    c. it is the dominant object on the Oklahoma landscape.
    d. all of the above.

5. At the end of the essay, Momaday goes

    a. to Rainy Mountain to visit his grandmother's grave.
    b. to see the Devil's Tower.
    c. back home to write about the Kiowa nation.

# CHAPTER 3: VOCABULARY QUIZ

### N. Scott Momaday, "The Way to Rainy Mountain"

NAME _____     DATE

Directions: Choose the correct definition for each of the following words.

## 1. DISPOSITION

    a. tendency or natural inclination
    b. the result of circumstances
    c. indifference

## 2. NOMADIC

    a. mentally unstable
    b. rooted or tied to one place
    c. wandering

## 3. RECKONED

    a. called
    b. estimated or judged
    c. referred to

## 4. TENUOUS

    a. shaky or flimsy
    b. certain
    c. stubborn

## 5. IMPALE

    a. to fix onto a point
    b. to paint a likeness of
    c. to carve into wood

William Least Heat Moon, "Nameless, Tennessee"

NAME _____     DATE

1. The town of Nameless, Tennessee, got its name

    a. by majority vote of its population of almost 90 people.
    b. by declaration from the Post Office Department.
    c. by default; the citizens couldn't agree on a name.

2. Least Heat Moon's chief reason for stopping in Nameless is

    a. to locate some distant relatives.
    b. to inquire about how the town got its unusual name.
    c. to buy gas and eat lunch.

3. Least Heat Moon describes an encounter that takes place

    a. at a general merchandise store.
    b. on the street corner.
    c. at the local diner where he has stopped for lunch.

4. The author captures some of the appeal of the Watts family

    a. by using numerous adjectives in his detailed physical descriptions.
    b. by reproducing their colorful speech through spelling some words as they sounded.
    c. by using the flashback technique.

5. Miss Ginny's Deathbook is

    a. a collection of old-fashioned home remedies.
    b. a record of her family tree.
    c. a chronological list of local deaths for the past twenty years.

# CHAPTER 3: VOCABULARY QUIZ

## William Least Heat Moon, "Nameless, Tennessee"

NAME _____     DATE

Directions: Choose the correct definition for each of the following words.

1. COMMENCED

    a. finished
    b. started or began
    c. marched forward

2. GAUNT

    a. thin and bony
    b. strong and healthy
    c. brave and determined

3. HOLLOWS

    a. valleys
    b. mountains
    c. woods

4. TRANSCRIBED

    a. reduced in size
    b. proofread for errors
    c. written out in full

5. INSCRIBIN' [INSCRIBING]

    a. photo-copying
    b. writing
    c. translating

# CHAPTER 3: CONTENT QUIZ

Terry Tempest Williams, "The Village Watchman"

NAME _____          DATE

1. The problem for the family taking care of Williams's Uncle Alan was not only that he was mentally handicapped but also that he had

    a. a violent temper.
    b. seizures that caused him to fall and hurt himself.
    c. the habit of wandering off and putting himself in danger.

2. Williams remembers Alan as being

    a. calm and very quiet.
    b. a person who expressed himself broadly and colorfully.
    c. hard to communicate with.

3. Physically, Alan was

    a. delicate and thin.
    b. short and pudgy.
    c. stocky and strong.

4. One incident Williams recalls is Alan's decision at the age of twenty-two to

    a. convert to Roman Catholicism.
    b. be baptized in the Mormon Church.
    c. abandon any belief in religion.

5. Williams relates that after his death, Alan came to her in a dream and said

    a. "I've learned what it means to be special."
    b. "I'm normal, perfectly normal."
    c. "We all must live with our handicaps."

# CHAPTER 3: VOCABULARY QUIZ

Terry Tempest Williams, "The Village Watchman"

NAME _____     DATE

Directions: Choose the correct definition for each of the following words.

1. MENTORS

    a. instructors or guides
    b. people who help resolve conflicts
    c. translators from one language to another

2. MEDIAN

    a. the proper way of doing something
    b. one who can predict the future
    c. a point exactly in the middle

3. SUBTLE

    a. soft and fuzzy, as a blanket
    b. delicate and refined, as a gesture
    c. hot and humid, as a summer day

4. FORMIDABLE

    a. physically imposing; frightening looking
    b. skillful at using one's hands; dextrous
    c. clumsy

5. CONVENED

    a. communicated
    b. came together
    c. called for help

# CHAPTER 3: CONTENT QUIZ

Scott Russell Sanders, "The Inheritance of Tools"

NAME _____       DATE

1. In this personal essay, Sanders discusses

    a. the monetary value of the tools he has inherited.
    b. memories evoked by his father's death.
    c. his personal expertise in using the tools he has inherited.

2. At the time of his father's death, Sanders was

    a. putting up a wall in the basement to make a bedroom for his daughter.
    b. building a cage for his daughter's gerbils.
    c. helping his father build cupboards for his brother.

3. Sanders especially values these tools because

    a. they are superior to the more modern versions.
    b. he inherited them from his father and his grandfather before him.
    c. they have become valuable antiques.
    d. all of the above.

4. Sanders' father taught him that it is extremely important to never use a saw

    a. without wearing gloves.
    b. without a First-Aid kit nearby.
    c. apart from a square.

5. Sanders states that the tools he inherited are a "double inheritance" because

    a. he now is passing the tools on to his own two children.
    b. along with the tools, he inherited the workbench.
    c. his father not only gave him the tools but also taught him how to use them.

# CHAPTER 3: VOCABULARY QUIZ

Scott Russell Sanders, "The Inheritance of Tools"

NAME _____     DATE

Directions: Choose the correct definition for each of the following words.

1. SPECULATING

    a. anticipating
    b. wishing
    c. guessing

2. LACERATE

    a. to mangle or tear
    b. to cut sharply
    c. to secure or tie down

3. BOTCHED

    a. spoiled or ruined
    b. cut
    c. fastened together

4. WIELD

    a. to encourage
    b. to complete
    c. to handle or use

5. PARED

    a. coupled satisfactorily
    b. reduced gradually
    c. worn through use

# CHAPTER 4: CONTENT QUIZ

## David Bodanis, "What's in Your Toothpaste"

NAME _____          DATE

1. The ingredient present in the largest quantity in toothpaste is

    a. water.
    b. chalk.
    c. titanium dioxide.

2. Chalk is added to toothpaste because

    a. it makes the toothpaste white.
    b. it colors or stains the teeth white.
    c. it grinds the teeth, removing stains and deposits.

3. The foam or suds that we associate with toothpaste comes from

    a. glycerine glycol.
    b. detergent.
    c. paraffin.
    d. none of the above.

4. The most common flavoring used in toothpaste is

    a. double rectified peppermint.
    b. spearmint oil.
    c. fruit oils.

5. Formaldehyde is used in toothpaste to

    a. make the mixture taste better.
    b. kill bacteria that might grow in the mixture.
    c. sweeten the mixture.
    d. all of the above.

# CHAPTER 4 : VOCABULARY QUIZ

## David Bodanis, "What's in Your Toothpaste"

NAME _____          DATE

Directions: Choose the correct definition for each of the following words.

1. LUCRATIVE

   a. profitable
   b. expensive
   c. easy

2. SOLUBLE

   a. capable of being dissolved
   b. capable of being discovered
   c. having an easy solution or answer

3. SAVOR

   a. to enjoy with appreciation
   b. to find distasteful
   c. to be able to afford

4. IRRESISTIBLE

   a. too weak to be attractive
   b. too powerful to be withstood
   c. easily avoided

5. INGEST

   a. to overrun, to swarm into
   b. to push aside
   c. to swallow or absorb

# CHAPTER 4: CONTENT QUIZ

## Barbara Ehrenreich, "In Defense of Talk Shows"

NAME _____     DATE

1. Ehrenreich believes that TV talk shows of the *Sally Jessy Raphael* variety are

    a. funny and entertaining
    b. highly moralistic
    c. the best thing on televison

2. Ehrenreich suggests that most of the guests who appear on these shows are

    a. presented sympathetically
    b. examples of middle-class morality
    c. preached at and shamed for their behavior

3. Ehrenreich also makes the point that the guests on these shows are often

    a. very much in control of their lives
    b. people who are poor or struggling financially
    c. people who are a lot smarter than they seem

4. In criticizing talk shows, Ehrenreich asks whether the next step would be to

    a. pay people to be publicly humiliated
    b. force the guests to be tarred and feathered
    c. bring on investment bankers and college professors

5. Ehrenreich is most sympathetic toward

    a. the kind of people who appear on talk shows
    b. people who find talk show participants vulgar
    c. conservative commentators like Bill Bennett and Joseph Lieberman

# CHAPTER 4: VOCABULARY QUIZ

Barbara Ehrenreich, "In Defense of Talk Shows"

NAME _____          DATE

Directions:  Choose the correct definition for each of the following words.

1. FRISSON

    a. moment of excitement
    b. compliment
    c. coolness; superior attitude

2. HECTORED

    a. tortured by guilt
    b. asked repeatedly
    c. harassed

3. LURID

    a. dangerous
    b. hidden away; closeted
    c. shocking; sensational

4. FECKLESS

    a. irresponsible
    b. rotten; inedible
    c. innocent

5. DETRACTORS

    a. people who put their noses in others' business
    b. snobs
    c. people who see no value in something

# CHAPTER 4: CONTENT QUIZ

## Aaron Copeland, "How We Listen to Music"

NAME _____          DATE

1. What does Copeland mean by the "sensuous plane"?

    a. the plane on which we literally feel the music
    b. the plane on which we feel the meaning behind the music
    c. the plane on which we hear the music without thinking about it

2. Who does Copeland believe is the better composer?

    a. Beethoven
    b. Tchaikovsky
    c. neither, he dislikes them both

3. Which plane does Copeland say most listeners are not conscious of?

    a. the first (sensuous)
    b. the second (expressive)
    c. the third (sheerly musical)

4. According to Copeland, listening to music on all three planes at once

    a. can be done only by musicians.
    b. is instinctive to everyone.
    c. is impossible.

5. According to Copeland, music

    a. has an expressive power.
    b. which always says the same thing will become dull.
    c. implies a subjective and an objective attitude to be listened to.
    d. all of the above

# CHAPTER 4: VOCABULARY QUIZ

Aaron Copeland, "How to Listen to Music"

NAME _____     DATE

Directions: Choose the correct definition for each of the following words.

## 1. POTENT

    a. effective
    b. over-powering
    c. ineffective

## 2. INHERENT

    a. foreign, out of place
    b. rare
    c. natural

## 3. RESIGNEDLY

    a. hysterically
    b. submissively
    c. aggressively

## 4. LAYMAN

    a. an amateur
    b. a member of the clergy
    c. a worker

## 5. DIGRESS

    a. to complain constantly
    b. to go off the point
    c. to agree

# CHAPTER 4: CONTENT QUIZ


Judith Ortiz Cofer, "The Myth of the Latin Woman"


NAME _____          DATE


1. When a young Englishman she didn't know sang "Maria" to Cofer on a bus full of passengers, Cofer

    a. took it as a compliment.
    b. reacted angrily.
    c. wasn't amused but responded politely.

2. One stereotype of Hispanic women that Cofer discusses is that of

    a. the devoted wife and mother.
    b. the sexual firebrand.
    c. the devout Catholic.

3. In noting cultural differences between Hispanic and Anglo women when she was younger, Cofer focuses on

    a. clothing and jewelry.
    b. attitudes toward religion.
    c. professional ambitions.

4. A second stereotype of Hispanic women that Cofer discusses is that of

    a. the chaste virgin.
    b. the talkative chatterbox.
    c. the domestic or menial worker.

5. Cofer says that her goal as a writer is to

    a. get back at people who would stereotype her.
    b. replace old stereotypes with more realistic images.
    c. show what negative results stereotypes can have.

# CHAPTER 4: VOCABULARY QUIZ

Judith Ortiz Cofer, "The Myth of the Latin Woman"

NAME _____     DATE

Directions:  Choose the correct definition for each of the following words.

1. SURVEILLANCE

   a. a kind of colorful skirt
   b. a close watch kept over someone or something
   c. an attempt to blend in with one's surroundings

2. PROSPECTIVE

   a. angle of vision
   b. thoughtful; intellectual
   c. relating to the future

3. PERPETUATED

   a. caused (something) to continue
   b. acted in a confused manner
   c. walked with a swaying motion of the hips

4. INNUENDO

   a. hint; allusion
   b. a kind of musical composition
   c. a person who speaks many languages

5. FAUX PAS

   a. a fur coat
   b. a mistake or social error
   c. an elegant restaurant

# CHAPTER 4: CONTENT QUIZ

## Bernard R. Berelson, "The Value of Children"

NAME _____        DATE

1. The purpose of Berelson's essay is to explain

    a. why people should or should not have children considering the tremendous expense involved.
    b. why people in these latter decades of the twentieth century want children.
    c. why all people in all societies have wanted children.

2. Berelson asserts that social traditions and social pressures

    a. greatly influence the number of children couples have.
    b. allow couples to have all the children they can physically have.
    c. are significant to persons of childbearing age for the first time in history.

3. Berelson says that generally, when the opportunity presents itself, both societies and families

    a. choose to have their children as soon as possible.
    b. choose a higher standard of living over a greater number of children.
    c. choose to establish themselves in a career before having children.

4. Berelson suggests that

    a. the childbearing patterns of the rural poor create unfair demands on the welfare system.
    b. childbearing is one of the few ways in which the poor can compete with the rich.
    c. the government should control the number of children couples are allowed to have.

5. To support his contention that some people want children as extensions of themselves, Berelson

    a. refers to a parable in the Bible.
    b. quotes from one of Shakespeare's sonnets.
    c. relates a personal experience.

# CHAPTER 4: VOCABULARY QUIZ

Bernard R. Berelson, "The Value of Children"

NAME _____    DATE

Directions: Choose the correct definition for each of the following words.

1. INNATELY

    a. selfishly
    b. naturally
    c. cheerfully

2. OBLITERATED

    a. praised profusely
    b. destroyed completely
    c. criticized unmercifully

3. EXPLICITLY

    a. definitely or clearly
    b. naturally
    c. practically

4. PROPITIATE

    a. to increase
    b. to appease or satisfy
    c. to reduce

5. ALTRUISTIC

    a. desirable
    b. unselfish
    c. abundant

# CHAPTER 4: CONTENT QUIZ

## Joseph Epstein, "What Are You Afraid of?"

NAME _____          DATE

1. Which is NOT one of Epstein's basic fears?

    a. fear of death
    b. fear of loss
    c. fear of intimacy
    d. fear of pain

2. Does Epstein mind that he has never really been tested by the terrors of war?

    a. yes
    b. no
    c. somewhat

3. According to Epstein, we live in an age when _____ has become the better part of _____.

    a. discretion; valor
    b. selfishness; life
    c. paranoia; fear

4. What is the deepest courage Epstein knows of?

    a. that required to give birth
    b. that required to raise a mentally damaged or emotionally disturbed child
    c. that required to go into battle in a war
    d. that required to die courageously

5. According to Epstein, courage consists in

    a. not wanting to embarrass yourself.
    b. knowing what to fear and acting on the knowledge.
    c. trusting in a higher power.

# CHAPTER 4: VOCABULARY QUIZ

Joseph Epstein, "What Are You Afraid of?"

NAME _____     DATE

Directions: Choose the correct definition for each of the following words.

1. SQUEAMISH

    a. extremely picky
    b. noisy
    c. easily offended

2. UNDULY

    a. excessively
    b. insanely
    c. constantly

3. ETHOS

    a. aura
    b. laws
    c. characteristic values or attitudes

4. LUCIDITY

    a. sanity
    b. clarity
    c. flexibility

5. RECOURSE

    a. consequences
    b. turning toward safety or a solution to a problem
    c. ramifications

Esmeralda Santiago, "Guavas"

NAME _____     DATE

1. Where is Santiago at the beginning of the essay?

    a. in Puerto Rico
    b. in a supermarket in New York
    c. at her home

2. According to Santiago, how do you eat a guava?

    a. You cut it into slices.
    b. You peel it and eat the center.
    c. You eat the skin but avoid the center.

3. With what does Santiago associate the guava?

    a. her home in Puerto Rico
    b. her childhood
    c. castor oil
    d. all of the above

4. How does Santiago narrate her essay?

    a. in the first person ("I")
    b. in the second person ("you")
    c. in the third person ("she")

5. At the end of the essay, what does Santiago do?

    a. She buys some guavas.
    b. She heads towards the apples and pears instead.
    c. She decides to re-visit Puerto Rico.

# CHAPTER 5: VOCABULARY QUIZ

Esmeralda Santiago, "Guavas"

NAME _____     DATE

Directions: Choose the correct definition for each of the following words.

1. PRICKLY

    a. having sharp, pointed projections
    b. sticky
    c. brightly colored

2. EMBEDDED

    a. loose
    b. firmly set or fixed
    c. self-contained

3. ENTICING

    a. exciting
    b. frightening
    c. dangerous

4. GRIMACE

    a. an imaginary creature
    b. a shout or cry
    c. a twisted or distorted facial expression

5. PURSE (verb)

    a. to draw the lips tightly together
    b. to put away
    c. to smile broadly

# CHAPTER 5: CONTENT QUIZ

William Zinsser, "The Transaction: Two Writing Processes"

NAME _____          DATE

1. Zinsser's thesis is that

    a. creative writing and expository writing are so dramatically different in style that they cannot be logically compared.
    b. professional writers must maintain a "professional approach" to their craft.
    c. there isn't any "right" way to do such intensely personal work.

2. The persons posing the questions to Zinsser and Dr. Brock were

    a. a group of students, English teachers, and parents.
    b. a group of cub reporters doing an interview for the local paper.
    c. a group of amateur writers attending a writing workshop.

3. Dr. Brock's philosophy of writing is

    a. "Let it all hang out!"
    b. "Revise, revise, revise!
    c. "Think, think, think!"

4. Dr. Brock says that

    a. it had never occurred to him that writing could be hard.
    b. he had never been depressed or unhappy.
    c. his approach to writing was "scientific."

5. Zinsser believes that most of the members of their audience

    a. left totally confused and perplexed.
    b. benefitted from the diversity of the writers' attitudes toward writing.
    c. were not at all interested in what the two writers had to say.

# CHAPTER 5: VOCABULARY QUIZ

William Zinsser, "The Transaction: Two Writing Processes"

NAME _____     DATE

Directions: Choose the correct definition for each of the following words.

1. VOCATION

    a. investment
    b. game of chance
    c. occupation or profession

2. AVOCATION

    a. hobby
    b. a calling or mission
    c. grueling work

3. ARDUOUS

    a. difficult
    b. amusing
    c. relaxing

4. DRUDGES

    a. obsessed or devoted followers
    b. people who do tedious work
    c. workers

5. BEWILDERED

    a. entertained
    b. exhausted
    c. perplexed

# CHAPTER 5: CONTENT QUIZ

## Mary Pipher, "Academic Selves"

NAME _____          DATE

1. Pipher's essay compares the experiences of boys and girls

    a. in college.
    b. on the job.
    c. in elementary, middle, and high school.

2. In the 1992 study that Pipher cites, boys are more likely to

    a. be seen as role models.
    b. receive the teacher's attention.
    c. speak up in class.
    d. all of the above

3. That study also found that girls' academic performances frequently decline

    a. in elementary school.
    b. in junior high school.
    c. during their junior and senior years.

4. When Pipher writes about young women's increasing focus on "affiliation" in junior high school, the term "affiliation" refers to

    a. family bonds.
    b. school loyalty.
    c. peer relationships.

5. Pipher understands the tendency of young women to hide their academic achievements in part because

    a. her sisters did the same thing.
    b. she did the same thing.
    c. she has extensively researched the problem.

# CHAPTER 5: VOCABULARY QUIZ

## Mary Pipher, "Academic Selves"

NAME _____          DATE

Directions: Choose the correct definition for each of the following words.


1. DOCILE

      a. aggressive
      b. immature
      c. easily managed

2. ROUTINELY

      a. regularly
      b. highly structured
      c. occasionally

3. ATTRIBUTED

      a. resulted from; assigned to
      b. contained within
      c. offered

4. PERSEVERE

      a. to criticize sharply
      b. to give up quickly
      c. to persist; to keep trying

5. FAMISHED

      a. intensely hungry
      b. satisfied
      c. poor

Suzanne Britt, "Neat People vs. Sloppy People"

NAME _____          DATE

1. According to Britt, what is the nature of the fundamental difference between neat and sloppy people?

    a. political
    b. moral
    c. psychological
    d. religious

2. According to Britt, sloppy people do all of the following except

    a. aim too high and wide.
    b. save everything.
    c. pay attention to detail.
    d. exhibit insensitivity.

3. Neat people, Britt says, only go through their mail

    a. when they are near a trash can.
    b. every other day.
    c. when they know a bill is coming.

4. Britt states that neat people like

    a. the process.
    b. the competition.
    c. the results.

5. One of Britt's neat person principles is

    a. cleanliness is next to godliness.
    b. throw everything away.
    c. any mess is a big mess.

# CHAPTER 5: VOCABULARY QUIZ

Suzanne Britt, "Neat People vs. Sloppy People"

NAME _____     DATE

Directions: Choose the correct definition for each of the following words.

1. CLOD

    a. a stupid or foolish person
    b. a brute
    c. a educated person

2. EXCAVATIONS

    a. submissions
    b. resentments
    c. unearthings

3. TENTATIVE

    a. paying attention
    b. permanent
    c. unsettled

4. SCRUPULOUSLY

    a. carefully
    b. casually
    c. anxiously

5. MEMENTO

    a. a candy
    b. a keepsake
    c. motion

# CHAPTER 5: CONTENT QUIZ

## Danzy Senna, "The Color of Love"

NAME _____     DATE

1. "The Color of Love" is about

    a. the author's relationship with her mother.
    b. the author's relationship with her grandmother.
    c. the author's search for someone to love.

2. What does Senna share with her grandmother?

    a. They both are painters.
    b. They both are musicians.
    c. They both are political activists.
    d. They both are writers.

3. Senna's grandmother was

    a. Protestant Irish.
    b. Catholic Italian.
    c. African American.

4. The fight that Senna has with her grandmother over her treatment of the maid marks

    a. the beginning of a new relationship between them.
    b. the end of their relationship.

5. What is the message that the grandmother writes on the paper as she is dying?

    a. that she loves Senna very much.
    b. that she hopes that Senna will forgive her for her bad behavior.
    c. It cannot be read; it is a faint, incomprehensible line.

# CHAPTER 5: VOCABULARY QUIZ

Danzy Senna, "The Color of Love"

NAME _____     DATE

Directions: Choose the correct definition for each of the following words.

1. CONFIDANTE

    a. a conspiracy
    b. a close, trusted friend
    c. a secret

2. BAFFLED

    a. puzzled; confused
    b. silenced
    c. sharpened; increased

3. ENTRENCHED

    a. securely established
    b. surrounded
    c. defended

4. RELIC

    a. something that survives from the past
    b. abandoned; forgotten
    c. broken

5. BANTERING

    a. fighting
    b. shouting
    c. teasing

# CHAPTER 5: CONTENT QUIZ

Meghan Daum, "Virtual Love"

NAME _____     DATE

1. Early in the essay, Daum confesses that she is

    a. a computer addict who is on line all the time.
    b. not what most people would call a computer person.
    c. someone who prefers talking with people over the telephone rather than writing to
them.

2. Pete first contacts Daum through

    a. a mutual friend.
    b. an e-mail message.
    c. a letter.

3. Their first "real" date occurs

    a. in New York just before Christmas.
    b. in Los Angeles in winter.
    c. in southern California in the summer.

4. In the course of the relationship, Daum discovered

    a. that a "virtual" romance was seductively attractive.
    b. that the "real" Pete was not like the "virtual" Pete.
    c. that e-mail fostered a romantic illusion.
    d. all of the above

5. What finally happened between Pete and Daum?

    a. They lost interest in each other.
    b. They got married.
    c. They are still dating.

# CHAPTER 5: VOCABULARY QUIZ

Meghan Daum, "Virtual Love"

NAME _____          DATE

Directions: Choose the correct definition for each of the following words.

## 1. INFATUATION

    a. a foolish or shallow attraction or love
    b. overweight
    c. juvenile or childlike behavior

## 2. ANTIDOTE

    a. a joke or humorous story
    b. a remedy to counteract a poison or unwanted condition
    c. an agent that fights against infection

## 3. REQUISITE

    a. unnecessary
    b. ordered ahead of time
    c. required; indispensable

## 4. SAVVY

    a. shrewdness; understanding
    b. sophistication; worldliness
    c. ignorance

## 5. SCENARIO

    a. a part of a stage or theater
    b. an outline or plan
    c. a coincidence; an unplanned event

Lars Eighner, "My Daily Dives in the Dumpster"

NAME _____          DATE

1. "Divers," Eighner argues, move through a "predictable series of stages" in learning to scavenge, including

    a. disgust and self-loathing.
    b. a compulsion to acquire everything they touch.
    c. a realization that they must restrict themselves to those things immediately useful.
    d. all of the above

2. Many people will salvage something from a dumpster, but what separates the amateur from the professional "diver" Eighner observes is

    a. eating discarded food.
    b. being willing to dive during daylight hours.
    c. taking only what one needs.
    d. all of the above

3. According to Eighner, can scroungers differ from scavengers in that

    a. they are people who must have small amounts of cash.
    b. they value only the cans and will ignore other valuable or usable items.
    c. both of the above

4. One important lesson Eighner mentions as having learned from his experiences in "diving" is

    a. that he will no longer have to work.
    b. that all material things are short-lived and not worth centering one's life around.
    c. that welfare supports could be reduced if more people were willing to scavenge.

5. According to Eighner, the wise "diver" shares with the very wealthy

    a. the fascination with constantly acquiring material goods.
    b. the realization that the quest for things is endless.
    c. the realization that people waste their talents.

# CHAPTER 6: VOCABULARY QUIZ

Lars Eighner, "My Daily Dives in the Dumpster"

NAME _____     DATE

Directions: Choose the correct definition for each of the following words.


1. NICHE

   a. profession; job
   b. place or position suitable to someone
   c. hobby

2. PRISTINE

   a. expensive; valuable
   b. unspoiled; untouched
   c. fragile

3. INTACT

   a. whole; unbroken
   b. spotted
   c. sticky

4. BEGRUDGE

   a. to resent
   b. to make difficult
   c. to give away

5. GAUDY

   a. expensive; precious
   b. old
   c. bright; showy

# CHAPTER 6: CONTENT QUIZ

Nora Ephron, "Revision and Life: Take It from the Top--Again"

NAME _____          DATE

1. The events in Ephron's essay are organized in

    a. a cause-and-effect pattern.
    b. chronological order.
    c. a comparison/contrast pattern.

2. Ephron first learned to revise when

    a. she was an undergraduate.
    b. she was a journalist.
    c. she was a screenplay writer.

3. Fiction, Ephron writes, is the "ultimate shot at revision" because

    a. fiction writing requires so much revision.
    b. fiction gives writers a chance to rework the events of their lives.
    c. fiction writers do not have deadlines and so can continue revising for as long as they
       wish.

4. According to Ephron, the major difference between writing fiction and writing screenplays is

    a. the amount of money that you are paid.
    b. the amount of work involved since writing screenplays is easier than writing fiction.
    c. the endpoint differs since a script is always a draft until the scene is shot.

5. Ephron's final advice to writers is

    a. revise now, before it's too late.
    b. never revise on a word processor.
    c. revise your conclusions as much as your introductions.
    d. all of the above

# CHAPTER 6: VOCABULARY QUIZ

### Nora Ephron, "Revision and Life: Take It from the Top--Again"

NAME _____                    DATE

Directions: Choose the correct definition for each of the following words.

1. CATAPULT

   a. to hurl or throw
   b. to move
   c. to lead

2. EXTRANEOUS

   a. extra or not essential
   b. spontaneous
   c. extreme

3. PLANE

   a. airplane
   b. level of development
   c. a well developed plan

4. MORBIDLY

   a. horribly or depressingly
   b. quickly
   c. sarcastically

5. EXHORTATION

   a. a loud cry
   b. a plea or warning
   c. a question

Diane Cole, "Don't Just Stand There"

NAME _____          DATE

1. If someone tells a joke that offends or ridicules you, you should

   a. laugh anyway since it would be embarrassing to object.
   b. respond in kind by telling a joke that offends or ridicules the thoughtless speaker.
   c. voice your anger calmly and pointedly.

2. Cole's essay explains how to deal with prejudice that reflects

   a. anti-Semitism.
   b. racism.
   c. sexism.
   d. all of the above

3. Voicing your objections to racial slurs and offensive ethnic jokes is important because it

   a. signals to the speaker the unacceptableness of such remarks
   b. reminds the speaker that such remarks are offensive, whether or not they were
      intentionally offensive
   c. makes you feel better
   d. all of the above

4. When you object to such remarks, you should indicate

   a. that your objections are based on principles.
   b. that your objections are based on how such remarks make you feel.
   c. that such discrimination might be against the law.

5. Cole's purpose(s) in writing the essay might have been

   a. to persuade people to think before they make potentially offensive jokes or remarks.
   b. to inform readers about ways in which they can respond in such situations.
   c. to offer parents some advice on helping their children cope with such situations.
   d. all of the above

# CHAPTER 6: VOCABULARY QUIZ

## Diane Cole, "Don't Just Stand There"

NAME _____     DATE

Directions: Choose the correct definition for each of the following words.

1. TINGED

   a. slightly colored by or mixed with
   b. slightly burned
   c. lacking in

2. SLUR

   a. remark meant to harm
   b. conflict
   c. compliment

3. BIASED

   a. unprejudiced
   b. ignorant
   c. prejudiced

4. RIFT

   a. an agreement
   b. an open break
   c. a physical conflict

5. DISCREETLY

   a. carefully or prudently
   b. openly
   c. loudly

# CHAPTER 6: CONTENT QUIZ

## David Brooks, "The Culture of Martyrdom"

NAME _____          DATE

1. Brooks' major purpose in the essay seems to be

    a. to argue for the expansion of the war against terrorism.
    b. to show how culture has created the process of martyrdom.
    c. to show how a Middle East peace settlement might be achieved.

2. Suicide bombing is

    a. a weapon that has been used for centuries.
    b. a relatively new thing, beginning roughly in the 1980s.

3. Typically, suicide bombers in Middle East are

    a. desperately poor and uneducated.
    b. mentally impaired or depressed.
    c. motivated by loyalty to their group.

4. According to Brooks, most Palestinians regard suicide bombings as

    a. an unacceptable form of political action.
    b. an acceptable means of resisting Israel.

5. Throughout the essay, Brooks likens the culture of martyrdom to

    a. a drug addiction.
    b. an illness or disease.
    c. a crime wave.
    d. none of the above.

# CHAPTER 6: VOCABULARY QUIZ

## David Brooks, "The Culture of Martyrdom"

NAME _____     DATE

Directions: Choose the correct definition for each of the following words.

### 1. DERAILING

    a. making stronger
    b. shouting at
    c. throwing off course; interrupting

### 2. RETALIATION

    a. a war plan
    b. a action taken for revenge or to "even" things up
    c. a recalculation; a new counting

### 3. COMMUNITARIAN

    a. selfish
    b. motivated by a system of religious beliefs
    c. an effort done by or for a community of people

### 4. HUMILIATED

    a. tricked
    b. degraded; embarrassed
    c. attacked

### 5. QUALMS

    a. doubts; misgivings
    b. moments of calmness or peace
    c. criticisms

# CHAPTER 6: CONTENT QUIZ

### Charlie Drozdyk, "Into the Loop: How to Get the Job You Want After Graduation"

NAME _____         DATE

1. According to Drozdyk, approximately two-thirds of all new jobs created in coming years will be in

    a. education.
    b. service industries.
    c. manufacturing.

2. Drozdyk says that bosses

    a. hate hiring people.
    b. usually choose candidates from the resumes they have received over the last six months.
    c. rarely interview more than two or three candidates.

3. In order to get your first job in most cases, Drozdyk believes it is essential to use

    a. common sense.
    b. connections.
    c. the services of a professional resume writer.

4. Drozdyk believes that interning and "temping" are

    a. not very helpful for getting a full-time paying job.
    b. excellent ways of entering the job market.
    c. options available to only a small number of job seekers.

5. According to one survey, nearly two-thirds of the people who interview and hire job applicants also consider the opinion of

    a. their own bosses.
    b. the personnel director.
    c. their administrative assistants.

# CHAPTER 6: VOCABULARY QUIZ

### Charlie Drozdyk, "Into the Loop: How to Get the Job You Want After Graduation"

NAME _____          DATE

Directions:  Choose the correct definition for each of the following words.

1. INEVITABLE

    a. unbelievable
    b. unusable; useless
    c. unavoidable; sure to happen

2. LOATHSOME

    a. unlikable; disgusting
    b. filled with good spirits; happy
    c. fearful; afraid

3. RESCIND

    a. take back; cancel
    b. restate in different words
    c. throw away; discard

4. COMMODITIES

    a. accomplishments; abilities
    b. things that are useful or valuable
    c. outside interests

5. ELUSIVE

    a. well-mannered
    b. difficult to find or hold onto
    c. dishonest; not to be trusted

# CHAPTER 6: CONTENT QUIZ

Jennifer Kahn, "Stripped for Parts"

NAME _____     DATE

1. Why is the "dead" man hooked up to "life-support" systems?

    a. Doctors hope to revive him.
    b. His family cannot accept his death.
    c. His body is a container in which organs are stored until they can be harvested.

2. According to an expert quoted in the essay, where does the future of transplantation lie?

    a. in using animal organs.
    b. in artificial organs.
    c. in the regeneration of cells.
    d. all of the above

3. Which situation best lends itself to organ harvesting and transplantation?

    a. brain death
    b. heart attacks
    c. comas

4. According to Kahn, medicine has always reserved its glory for

    a. the doctors.
    b. the patients.
    c. the living.

5. Kahn says that the endurance athletes of medicine are

    a. brain surgeons.
    b. transplant doctors.
    c. heart doctors.

# CHAPTER 6: VOCABULARY QUIZ

Jennifer Kahn, "Stripped for Parts"

NAME _____     DATE

Directions: Choose the correct definition for each of the following words.

1. FINESSE

    a. finality
    b. skill
    c. energy

2. CADAVER

    a. a corpse
    b. an organ
    c. a patient

3. OBSOLETE

    a. outdated
    b. isolated
    c. functional

4. CASCADE

    a. trickle
    b. a gush
    c. a steady stream

5. PROCUREMENT

    a. containment
    b. regeneration
    c. acquisition

# CHAPTER 7: CONTENT QUIZ

## E. M. Forster, "My Wood"

NAME _____          DATE

1. To explain the consequences of owning property, Forster relies heavily on

    a. a book he wrote about the English in India.
    b. historical and psychological research.
    c. personal experience and observation.

2. In Forster's essay, he is concerned with

    a. the economic effects of owning property.
    b. the political aspects of owning property.
    c. the psychological effects of owning property.

3. One disadvantage of Forster's property is

    a. it is quite heavily wooded.
    b. it has a public footpath cutting across it.
    c. it is very expensive to maintain.

4. Forster says property produces

    a. men of weight.
    b. men of wealth.
    c. men of wit and wisdom.

5. According to Forster's opinion, property makes its owner feel that he ought to do something to it because

    a. he feels compelled to make it more economically profitable.
    b. he has a desire to express his personality.
    c. he earnestly wishes to make it more beautiful.

# CHAPTER 7: VOCABULARY QUIZ

E. M. Forster, "My Wood"

NAME _____     DATE

Directions: Choose the correct definition for each of the following words.

## 1. PRETENTIOUS

   a. undesirable
   b. insincere
   c. limitless

## 2. SHUN

   a. to avoid
   b. to retain
   c. to handle

## 3. CARNAL

   a. fun-filled
   b. fleshy or worldly
   c. evil

## 4. TRAVERSES

   a. cross
   b. diminishes
   c. encircles

## 5. AVARICIOUS

   a. generous
   b. greedy
   c. possessive

# CHAPTER 7: CONTENT QUIZ


Joan Jacobs Brumberg, "The Origins of Anorexia Nervosa"


NAME _____          DATE


1. Anorexia nervosa is an eating disorder that was first described

   a. in the 1970's.
   b. in the 17th century.
   c. in the 19th century.

2. According to Brumberg, those most likely to exhibit the symptoms of anorexia nervosa are

   a. young women from middle-class or upper-class families.
   b. young men and women.
   c. young women living in poverty.

3. Brumberg suggests that anorexia nervosa occurred in Victorian society because

   a. such behavior was a socially acceptable way in which a child might effectively manipulate parents.
   b. eating habits during the period were particularly bad.
   c. families no longer had the time to sit down to eat together.

4. Refusing to eat, as an emotional tactic, has meaning only in situations in which

   a. food is plentiful.
   b. food is a symbol of parents' love.
   c. food is attractive or pleasing.
   d. food is prepared by someone other than the person refusing.
   e. all of the above

5. Brumberg's purpose in the essay seems to be to

   a. persuade her audience to beware of the dangers of anorexia nervosa.
   b. warn her audience of the signs of anorexia nervosa.
   c. suggest a possible treatment plan for anorexics.
   d. none of the above

# CHAPTER 7: VOCABULARY QUIZ

### Joan Jacobs Brumberg, "The Origins of Anorexia Nervosa"

NAME _____          DATE

Directions: Choose the correct definition for each of the following words.

1. BOURGEOIS

    a. upper class
    b. lower class
    c. middle class

2. DEEMED

    a. thought or considered
    b. called
    c. saved

3. AFFRONT

    a. to insult or offend openly
    b. to humor
    c. to disturb

4. PREROGATIVE

    a. habit
    b. prohibition
    c. privilege

5. FILIAL

    a. due or coming from a child
    b. due or coming from a parent
    c. unquestioning

# CHAPTER 7: CONTENT QUIZ

Andres Martin, "Of Teenagers and Tattoos"

NAME _____        DATE

1. Martin argues that tattoos can be interpreted

    a. as proof of toughness and machismo.
    b. as acts of rebellion.
    c. as desires to memorialize dearly held persons or concepts.
    d. all of the above

2. According to Martin, understanding why teenagers choose to get tattoos can also

    a. be a way of better understanding teenagers.
    b. solve other parent-child clashes.
    c. stop teenagers from getting tattoos and piercings.

3. Martin surmises that the anchor was a popular tattoo because of its association with

    a. endurance.
    b. power.
    c. boats.
    d. stability.

4. Martin's first "Case Vignette" involves

    a. a husband and wife with matching tattoos.
    b. a thirteen-year-old boy who wanted to memorialize his dead father.
    c. a runaway teenager.
    d. none of the above

5. Among the individuals who Martin believes get tattoos for fleeting reasons are

    a. hospitalized or incarcerated youth.
    b. children from wealthy families.
    c. teenagers with many brothers and sisters.

# CHAPTER 7: VOCABULARY QUIZ

Andres Martin, "On Teenagers and Tattoos"

NAME _____     DATE

Directions: Choose the correct definition for each of the following words.

## 1. CONSTRUE

    a. to refuse
    b. to interpret
    c. to misunderstand

## 2. SEMBLANCE

    a. outside
    b. tendency
    c. likeness

## 3. TRANSIENT

    a. temporary
    b. unimportant
    c. aimless

## 4. INDELIBLY

    a. unbelievably
    b. temporarily
    c. permanently

## 5. ARBITER

    a. contestant
    b. authority
    c. spectator

# CHAPTER 7: CONTENT QUIZ

## Brent Staples, "Black Men and Public Space"

NAME _____     DATE

1. The fear that Staples elicits from passersby is occasioned by

    a. his race.
    b. his gender.
    c. his youth.
    d. his physical size.
    e. all of the above

2. The experiences about which Staples writes occur

    a. at night in relatively deserted urban areas.
    b. in any "public" space.
    c. in white suburban neighborhoods at night.

3. When Staples writes about "public" spaces, he is referring to

    a. park areas open to the public.
    b. city streets and sidewalks.
    c. restaurants and hotel lobbies.
    d. all of the above

4. The reactions of other pedestrians to his presence make Staples feel

    a. alienated from those he encounters.
    b. aware of the dangers that surround him.
    c. conscious of the stereotyped image by which he is judged.
    d. all of the above

5. Now when Staples walks late at night, he

    a. makes sure that he is wearing a coat and tie.
    b. avoids deserted streets.
    c. whistles selections from classical music.

# CHAPTER 7: VOCABULARY QUIZ

Brent Staples, "Black Men and Public Space"

NAME _____     DATE

Directions: Choose the correct definition for each of the following words.

1. AFFLUENT

   a. prosperous
   b. diverse
   c. easily accessible

2. SEEPED

   a. poured
   b. leaked or slowly moved
   c. wandered

3. AVID

   a. enthusiastic
   b. addicted
   c. frequent

4. PERILOUS

   a. unequaled
   b. exciting
   c. dangerous

5. STEELY

   a. hard
   b. nervous
   c. aggressive

# CHAPTER 7: CONTENT QUIZ

Veronica Chambers, "Dreadlocked"

NAME _____          DATE

1. Chambers refers to her hair as "bad" because

    a. "bad" really means "good."
    b. it is thick and coarse.
    c. she wears dreadlocks.

2. Why does Chambers wear dreadlocks?

    a. They require little time or care.
    b. They are fashionable.
    c. They allow her to see beauty where no one had seen beauty before.

3. Dreadlocks, Chambers observes,

    a. confer many roles on her.
    b. provoke a wide range of responses from people.
    c. suggest that she is a lot more interesting than she is.
    d. all of the above

4. What event lead to Chambers' first dreadlocks?

    a. her frustration with hairdressers.
    b. a broken heart when a boy doesn't call.
    c. her vacation in Jamaica.

5. Wearing dreadlocks has been for Chambers

    a. a great frustration.
    b. a way of changing how she sees herself.
    c. a way of making a political statement.

# CHAPTER 7: VOCABULARY QUIZ

## Veronica Chambers, "Dreadlocked"

NAME _____          DATE

Directions:  Choose the correct definition for each of the following words.


1. HYPE

    a. a type of needle
    b. exaggerated publicity
    c. secretness

2. AFOREMENTIONED

    a. spoken of before
    b. pretended; play-acted
    c. coming afterwards; followed

3. PREVALENT

    a. widely existing; common
    b. coming before
    c. uncommon

4. KINKY

    a. tightly curled
    b. tied up with rope
    c. made up of several different colors

5. CHARITABLY

    a. suddenly
    b. freely
    c. generously; kindly

Malcolm Gladwell, "The Trouble with Fries"

NAME _____          DATE

1. According to Gladwell, how many pounds of French fries does the average American consume annually?

      a. about 4 pounds
      b. about 15 pounds
      c. about 30 pounds

2. Which of the following fats is most dangerous to our health?

      a. polyunsaturated fats
      b. saturated fats
      c. trans unsaturated fats

3. The "French-fry problem" could be solved by

      a. an advertising campaign that warned people not to eat French fries.
      b. cooking the fries in oil that is not as dangerous to people's health.
      c. taxing French fries like cigarettes since both are a health hazard.

4. Why wasn't McDonald's McLean Deluxe a commercial success?

      a. People didn't like its taste.
      b. It cost more than a regular hamburger.
      c. People didn't want a healthy fast food.

5. For a more healthy French fry to be successful, Gladwell argues, it should be marketed as

      a. the "healthy" fry.
      b. the "low fat" fry.
      c. the "better" or "classic" fry.

# CHAPTER 7: VOCABULARY QUIZ

## Malcolm Gladwell, "The Trouble with Fries"

NAME _____     DATE

Directions: Choose the correct definition for each of the following words.

1. ASTOUNDED

    a. ordered; commanded
    b. wounded
    c. surprised; amazed

2. OPTIMAL

    a. related to the eye, to seeing
    b. least
    c. best

3. INTERSPERSED

    a. scattered among
    b. decreased
    c. separated

4. WREAK

    a. to destroy; to damage
    b. to complete
    c. to make whole

5. GRAVITATE

    a. to be attracted to; to move toward
    b. to become heavier
    c. to regard seriously

Ben Stein, "How Can Anyone Who Lives in Insane Luxury Be a Star in Today's World"

NAME _____        DATE

1. Does Stein now think that it matters who eats at Morton's?

    a. yes
    b. no

2. According to Stein, who is a real hero?

    a. coal miners
    b. CEOs making millions
    c. the U.S. soldier

3. What has become Stein's main task in life?

    a. to write the best he can
    b. to donate money to charity
    c. to be a civic-minded member of society
    d. to be a good father, son, and husband

4. With what does Stein no longer feel comfortable?

    a. being a part of a system with poor values
    b. the extremist politics of today
    c. working for a celebrity E-zine

5. Stein says that we must turn the power over to

    a. the President.
    b. God.
    c. Congress.
    d. the people.

# CHAPTER 8: VOCABULARY QUIZ

Ben Stein, "How Can Anyone Who Lives in Insane Luxury Be a Star in Today's World"

NAME _____     DATE

Directions: Choose the correct definition for each of the following words.

1. DROVES

    a. occasional visitors
    b. arriving in automobiles
    c. crowds

2. DESOLATE

    a. abandoned
    b. abnormal; varying from what is considered normal
    c. compulsive

3. LAVISH

    a. petty
    b. extravagant
    c. enjoyable

4. GRATITUDE

    a. attention
    b. appreciation
    c. understanding

5. PARAPHRASE

    a. to quote
    b. to pause
    c. to put into your own words

# CHAPTER 8: CONTENT QUIZ

Judy Brady, "I Want a Wife"

NAME _____          DATE

1. In this essay Brady defines "wife"

    a. by using the denotative dictionary definition.
    b. by giving examples of what women look for in a "good marriage."
    c. by delineating the stereotypical male demands in marriage.

2. Brady makes her point through the use of

    a. an autobiographical narrative.
    b. a series of case histories.
    c. personal experience and observation.

3. The core of Brady's essay consists of seven different categories of

    a. items that should be addressed in a prenuptial agreement.
    b. duties that a wife typically performs.
    c. criteria that could be considered grounds for divorce.

4. In her essay, Brady seems to be trying to make vivid

    a. the hazard of marriage.
    b. the inequality that can or does exist in a conventional marriage.
    c. the role of the modern wife.

5. A synonym for Brady's concept of the word "wife" could be

    a. servant.
    b. partner.
    c. homemaker.

# CHAPTER 8: VOCABULARY QUIZ

Judy Brady, "I Want a Wife"

NAME _____     DATE

Directions: Choose the correct definition for each of the following words.

## 1. RAMBLING

    a. constant
    b. wandering without particular aim
    c. nagging

## 2. REPLENISHED

    a. made full or complete again
    b. rendered useless
    c. made invaluable

## 3. ENTAIL

    a. supervise or take charge
    b. involve or necessitate
    c. remove or destroy

## 4. ADHERENCE

    a. adequate preparation
    b. devotion and support
    c. passive attitude

## 5. MONOGAMY

    a. giving one's consent
    b. being a compatible partner
    c. having only one mate

# CHAPTER 8: CONTENT QUIZ

## Robin D. G. Kelley, "The People in Me"

NAME _____     DATE

1. With what question does Kelley begin his essay?

   a. So, what are you?
   b. Who were my ancestors?
   c. What is distinctive about your culture?

2. What does Kelley's title, "The People in Me," refer to?

   a. the different roles that he plays
   b. how his personality reflects his ancestors
   c. how he is the product of different cultures

3. In the first part of the essay, Kelley draws his examples from

   a. published research.
   b. interviews with scholars.
   c. his own family.
   d. none of the above

4. Which word does Kelley prefer?

   a. multicultural
   b. multiethnic
   c. polycultural

5. Black culture, Kelley notes, has always been

   a. fluid and hybrid.
   b. pure and discrete.
   c. easily separated from the other cultures that surround it.

# CHAPTER 8: VOCABULARY QUIZ

## Robin D. G. Kelley, "The People in Me"

NAME _____     DATE

Directions: Choose the correct definition for each of the following words.

1. INDIGNITIES

    a. insults; unjust actions
    b. compliments
    c. inadequacies; shortcomings

2. FLUENT

    a. able to write or speak easily
    b. angry
    c. loud

3. DISCRETE

    a. interrelated; connected
    b. taken as a whole
    c. separate; distinct

4. HYBRID

    a. pure
    b. anything of mixed origins
    c. weak or powerless

5. PANTHEON

    a. people who are looked up to; important historical figures
    b. ordinary people
    c. religious leaders

# CHAPTER 8: CONTENT QUIZ

## Amy Tan, "Mother Tongue"

NAME _____          DATE

1. Tan's mother's command of formal English

   a. made Tan, as a younger woman, ashamed of her mother.
   b. resulted in people not taking her mother seriously.
   c. made it difficult for her mother to get prompt attention from others.
   d. all of the above

2. Tan herself speaks

   a. only in formal English.
   b. in her mother's "tongue" only when she is with her mother.
   c. neither of the above

3. The examples that Tan cites in her essay are drawn from

   a. extensive research in linguistics and sociology.
   b. interviews with a wide range of experts.
   c. her own experiences and observations.

4. Tan wonders if other Asian American children might have been drawn to mathematics and engineering and not to creative writing because

   a. they, as a whole, always do significantly better on math achievement tests than in English.
   b. their teachers might have steered them away from writing and into math and science.
   c. their language skills are shaped by their family environment.
   d. all of the above

5. As she developed as a writer, Tan came to regard her mother's broken English as

   a. a constant embarrassment.
   b. a handicap that she would have to overcome.
   c. a vital part of her own English.

# CHAPTER 8: VOCABULARY QUIZ

## Amy Tan, "Mother Tongue"

NAME _____     DATE

Directions: Choose the correct definition for each of the following words.

1. WINCE

    a. to admire proudly
    b. to laugh quietly
    c. to shrink back, usually with embarrassment

2. EMPIRICAL

    a. fluctuating, ever changing
    b. based on observation and experience
    c. based on abstract rules or principles

3. GUISE

    a. fixed position
    b. fundamental or unchangeable character
    c. pretended appearance; disguise

4. IMPECCABLE

    a. halting; hesitant
    b. flawless
    c. guiltless; innocent

5. SEMANTIC

    a. connected with the meaning of a word
    b. connected with the structure of a word
    c. connected with the sound of a word

# CHAPTER 8: CONTENT QUIZ

John Hollander, "Mess"

NAME _____          DATE

1. Hollander says that the kind of mess he is most afflicted with is

    a. his neglected garden.
    b. the mess he creates in his kitchen.
    c. the mess in his workplace.

2. Originally, the word mess referred to

    a. a serving of food or a course in a meal.
    b. a kind of porridge or mush.
    c. a collapsed building.

3. According to Hollander, messiness may be inevitable when

    a. people today are so busy.
    b. people have so many things in their lives.
    c. people aren't trained to be neat when they are children.

4. Hollander says that describing a mess

    a. is almost impossible to do.
    b. is one of his favorite things to do as a writer.
    c. is a way of imposing order on it.

5. Hollander ends his essay by describing

    a. his cat in his office.
    b. the pile of folders and papers on top of his computer.
    c. his dream of a perfectly ordered world.

# CHAPTER 8: VOCABULARY QUIZ

## John Hollander, "Mess"

NAME _____     DATE

Directions: Choose the correct definition for each of the following words.

1. EPHEMERAL

   a. down-to-earth; practical
   b. having to do with the heavens
   c. lasting a very short time

2. CHAOS

   a. a spicy stew or minestrone
   b. a state of complete confusion
   c. a very fast musical composition

3. ASKEW

   a. questioning; looking for answers
   b. hanging on a wall
   c. crooked; out of line

4. PIQUE

   a. the very top of something
   b. a brief feeling of anger or resentment
   c. a pinch or squeeze

5. DISDAIN

   a. to look on with scorn
   b. to praise or compliment
   c. to challenge, as to a fight

# CHAPTER 8: CONTENT QUIZ

## Margaret Atwood, "The Female Body"

NAME _____          DATE

1. Atwood defines her subject in the essay by

    a. developing a single example.
    b. arguing for a particular view of her subject.
    c. offering a variety of perspectives on her subject.

2. The examples of the female body that Atwood gives include

    a. a transparent "scientific" model.
    b. a doll for young girls.
    c. everyday objects made to resemble the female body.
    d. all of the above

3. Atwood's tone in the essay could best be characterized as

    a. serious and informative.
    b. playful and sarcastic.
    c. angry and argumentative.

4. For Atwood, the typical male response to a female is

    a. to love and admire.
    b. to sexually desire and wish to control or dominate.
    c. to create an equal partnership.

5. Toward the end of the essay, when she contrasts the female and male brains, Atwood is

    a. reporting a scientific fact.
    b. reporting a widespread folk belief.
    c. playing with popular stereotypes attributed to the behavior and values of women and men.
    d. none of the above

# CHAPTER 8: VOCABULARY QUIZ

## Margaret Atwood, "The Female Body"

NAME _____          DATE

Directions: Choose the correct definition for each of the following words.

1. CAPACIOUS

   a. capable
   b. able to contain much; roomy
   c. offensive

2. SCUTTLING

   a. moving quickly
   b. moving slowly
   c. moving awkwardly

3. BOTCHED

   a. ruined; spoiled
   b. perfect; exemplary
   c. expensive

4. SHODDY

   a. messy
   b. valuable
   c. cheap; inferior

5. VOID

   a. the stars
   b. the universe
   c. empty space

# CHAPTER 9: CONTENT QUIZ

## Katherine Porter, "The Value of a College Degree"

NAME _____        DATE

1. More highly educated women show a tendency to

    a. postpone marriage and child-rearing.
    b. spend less time with their children.
    c. spend more time with their children.
    d. prefer co-habitation to marriage.

2. Research has shown that parental educational levels are directly connected to

    a. the health status of the couple's children.
    b. their children's selfishness and materialism.
    c. their children's emotional dependency on the parents.

3. Students who attend a post-secondary institution tend to be

    a. more open-minded.
    b. less prejudiced.
    c. less authoritarian.
    d. all of the above

4. Which of the following is NOT a benefit to society from a more-educated population?

    a. increased tax revenues
    b. greater worker productivity
    c. decreased reliance on governmental support
    d. a population more likely to agree with governmental policies

5. Given the increasing costs of college and the rising rates of interest on student loans, Porter argues that students should carefully consider whether or not college makes financial sense.

    a. true
    b. false

# CHAPTER 9: VOCABULARY QUIZ

Katherine Porter, "The Value of a College Degree"

NAME _____     DATE

Directions: Choose the correct definition for each of the following words.

1. MONETARY

    a. lasting only a short while
    b. showy; obvious
    c. financial

2. NOTION

    a. idea
    b. chance
    c. fact

3. MOBILITY

    a. subject to death
    b. able to change
    c. stability

4. SUFFICIENTLY

    a. essentially
    b. confidently
    c. adequately

5. SIZEABLE

    a. adjustable
    b. fairly large
    c. very small

# CHAPTER 9: CONTENT QUIZ

### Linda Lee, "The Case Against College"

NAME _____        DATE

1. In the United States what percentage of high school graduates go on to college?

   a. 20%
   b. 66%
   c. 80%

2. How does Lee seem to feel about that percentage?

   a. It's too low; everyone ought to have the opportunity to go to college.
   b. It's too high, not everyone is ready for college or needs college.
   c. It's just about right.

3. Lee's primary example in the essay is taken from

   a. the recommendation of an expert panel of educators and business executives.
   b. her son's experiences.
   c. her own experiences.

4. What percentage of college students receive their degrees within four years?

   a. 26%
   b. 39%
   c. 80%

5. To whom does Lee seem to be writing–that is, who is her audience?

   a. college presidents and state legislators
   b. parents of high school students
   c. college students
   d. returning adult students

# CHAPTER 9: VOCABULARY QUIZ

Linda Lee, "The Case Against College"

NAME _____     DATE

Directions: Choose the correct definition for each of the following words.

## 1. OBSESSED

    a. preoccupied; focused on
    b. wounded; hurt
    c. connected to

## 2. PONDER

    a. to steal
    b. to consider carefully
    c. to declare

## 3. PIT

    a. to favor one over another
    b. to relate as equals
    c. to set as rivals

## 4. MINUS

    a. feeling uneasy or sick
    b. a penalty
    c. less; without

## 5. BONUS

    a. an obligation
    b. a financial reward
    c. a good deed

# CHAPTER 9: CONTENT QUIZ

## Ronna Vanderslice, "When I Was Young an A Was an A"

NAME _____          DATE

1. According to Vanderslice, grade inflation may

    a. give students an incorrect view of their own competence.
    b. minimize the effectiveness of grades as indicators of excellence.
    c. complicate questions of what an A means.
    d. all of the above

2. Vanderslice cites the example of Harvard professor Harvey Mansfield who gives the students two grades:

    a. one for the student and one for the parents.
    b. one for the public record and one for the student's private use.
    c. one for effort and one for achievement.

3. Vanderslice argues that by rewarding mediocrity we

    a. encourage students to feel good about themselves.
    b. recognize that students have spent a considerable amount of money on their educations.
    c. discourage excellence.
    d. undermine America's technological expertise.

4. According to Vanderslice, what percent of college students receive grades lower than B-?

    a. 5-7 %
    b. 10-15%
    c. 20-25%
    d. 30-35%

5. Which of the following is NOT one of Vanderslice's recommendations?

    a. starting all students with an F and have them work toward an A
    b. reviewing standards for grading
    c. assessing the validity of student-opinion surveys
    d. having faculty insist that standards are part of the academic ethic

# CHAPTER 9: VOCABULARY QUIZ

Ronna Vanderslice, "When I Was Young an A Was an A"

NAME _____     DATE

Directions: Choose the correct definition for each of the following words.

1. RIGOR

    a. stiffness
    b. difficulty
    c. ease

2. VALID

    a. useful
    b. necessary
    c. sound; correct

3. DIFFERENTIATE

    a. to distinguish among
    b. to make different
    c. to decide

4. DISCIPLINES

    a. challenges
    b. corrections
    c. areas of study

5. CONSEQUENCE

    a. an incorrect sequence
    b. a result
    c. a purpose

# CHAPTER 9: CONTENT QUIZ

## Alfie Kohn, "The Dangerous Myth of Grade Inflation"

NAME _____        DATE

1. According to Kohn, what must be looked at to get an accurate picture in grade changes?

    a. students' socioeconomic backgrounds
    b. students' transcripts
    c. students' gender

2. Kohn considers the SAT an accurate indicator of how students will do in college.

    a. true
    b. false

3. What does Kohn say are the two types of motivation?

    a. monetary and intellectual
    b. forced and unforced
    c. intrinsic and extrinsic
    d. parental and self

4. When do many people say that they began to "explore ideas deeply and passionately"?

    a. in graduate school
    b. after they choose their major
    c. by their junior year
    d. when their grades begin to improve

5. According to Kohn, what is a focus on grades likely to do?

    a. decrease their importance
    b. undermine a love of learning
    c. create more A students

# CHAPTER 9: VOCABULARY QUIZ

Alfie Kohn, "The Dangerous Myth of Grade Inflation"

NAME _____          DATE

Directions:  Choose the correct definition for each of the following words.


1. POSTURE

    a. mannerism
    b. behavior
    c. attitude

2. DISCLOSED

    a. ended
    b. criticized
    c. uncovered

3. BENCHMARK

    a. a conclusion
    b. a reference point
    c. a perspective or viewpoint

4. CREDO

    a. a belief
    b. a practical joke
    c. a lie

5. PEDAGOGY

    a. a judgement
    b. a child molester
    c. a method of teaching

# CHAPTER 9: CONTENT QUIZ

Sister Helen Prejean, "Memoirs of a Dead Man Walking"

NAME _____          DATE

1. Who played Prejean in the film version of her story?

    a. Jodie Foster
    b. Cybill Shepherd
    c. Susan Sarandon
    d. Sally Field

2. What was the original role that Prejean played in Sonnier's life?

    a. pen pal
    b. spiritual advisor
    c. psychologist
    d. social worker

3. What was Prejean's "bad mistake"?

    a. getting close to Sonnier
    b. not meeting the victim's family sooner
    c. hearing Sonnier's confession

4. According to Prejean, what is the essential torture of the death penalty?

    a. the physical pain
    b. the heartbreak of the victim's family
    c. the shame
    d. the anticipation of death

5. Prejean's upbringing fostered in her an awareness of the politics of race.

    a. true
    b. false

# CHAPTER 9: VOCABULARY QUIZ

Sister Helen Prejean, "Memoirs of a Dead Man Walking"

NAME _____     DATE

Directions: Choose the correct definition for each of the following words.

1. ASSUAGE

    a. to avoid
    b. to ignore
    c. to ease

2. PROTOCOL

    a. procedure
    b. recommendation
    c. rule book

3. STEREOTYPICAL

    a. double vision
    b. not individualized
    c. unusual

4. BEDROCK

    a. background
    b. foundation
    c. prescribed order

5. MUSTER

    a. to attempt
    b. to claim
    c. to collect or gather together

# CHAPTER 9: CONTENT QUIZ

## David Gelernter, "What Do Murderers Deserve?"

NAME _____      DATE

1. According to Gelernter, we should execute murderers because

    a. we want to deter other people from committing murder.
    b. we want to avenge the victim.
    c. we want to make a communal proclamation that murder is intolerable.

2. For Gelernter, a life sentence for murder is just as appropriate as a death sentence

    a. true
    b. false

3. Throughout the essay, Gelernter uses two specific examples--Karla Faye Tucker and Ted Kaczynski. What does Gelernter see as the main difference between the two?

    a. one was penitent, but executed; one was impenitent, but was not executed
    b. that where you are tried--geographically--determines the sentence you receive
    c. that one was a woman and the other a man

4. According to Gelernter, our unwillingness to execute murderers can be attributed to our

    a. uncertainty about the fairness of the trials murderers receive.
    b. feeling that executions are barbaric and uncivilized.
    c. fear of being judgmental.

5. Are there any circumstances under which Gelernter thinks that a life sentence for murder might be more appropriate than the death penalty?

    a. absolutely not
    b. only if the killer is truly penitent
    c. only if every legal avenue has been tried unsuccessfully

# CHAPTER 9: VOCABULARY QUIZ

David Gelernter. "What Do Murderers Deserve?"

NAME _____          DATE

Directions: Choose the correct definition for each of the following words.

## 1. DETERRING

    a. discouraging an action
    b. turning a decision over to someone else
    c. preventing

## 2. DEFILES

    a. refuses to do something
    b. pollutes; makes dirty
    c. accuses

## 3. STEEL

    a. to take something without permission
    b. to make oneself hard or unfeeling
    c. to act

## 4. UNAMBIGUOUSLY

    a. clearly; certainly
    b. unclearly
    c. loudly

## 5. FLUBBED

    a. messed up; botched
    b. cleaned up
    c. done; completed

# CHAPTER 9: CONTENT QUIZ

## Martin Luther King, Jr. "I Have a Dream"

NAME _____     DATE

1. King's beginning with "Five score years ago" is an allusion to

    a. Lincoln's Emancipation Proclamation.
    b. Lincoln's Gettysburg Address.
    c. the Constitution of the United States.

2. King's thesis is that, despite the Emancipation Proclamation and the democratic foundation of the U.S. government,

    a. increasing numbers of blacks are political hostages.
    b. "creative suffering" has not worked; we must change our strategy immediately.
    c. black people are still not free; they should work peacefully but incessantly toward achieving equality.

3. King's address was delivered to a large audience on the occasion of

    a. the dedication of the Lincoln Memorial.
    b. King's receiving the Nobel Peace Prize.
    c. the "March on Washington."

4. King says America has "defaulted" on the promises made to all Americans by the founding fathers of our country, which were

    a. the rights of life, liberty, and the pursuit of happiness.
    b. diplomatic immunity and immediate release of all prisoners.
    c. the rights to amass material wealth and political power.

5. King builds momentum through the repetitive use of the phrase (at least 12 times) in the final paragraph of his address:

    a. "One hundred years later..."
    b. "Let freedom ring..."
    c. "Free at last!"

# CHAPTER 9: VOCABULARY QUIZ

## Martin Luther King, Jr., "I Have a Dream"

NAME _____     DATE

Directions: Choose the correct definition for each of the following words.

1. LANGUISHING

    a. hoping
    b. lingering
    c. staggering

2. DEFAULTED

    a. prepared to return
    b. promised to remember
    c. failed to pay

3. DEGENERATE

    a. to enhance
    b. to deteriorate or to decline
    c. to forego or to pass by

4. SWELTERING

    a. suffering or oppressed from
    b. coping or surviving
    c. confined or bound by

5. PRODIGIOUS

    a. tremendous
    b. hilarious or very funny
    c. revered or honored

Richard Rodriguez, "None of This Is Fair"

NAME _____          DATE

1. Rodriguez has benefitted from Affirmative Action, but admits that

    a. because he was a "minority student," he continued to be a victim of racism throughout all his years of schooling.
    b. the disadvantages of other Mexican-Americans permitted his own advancement as a "minority student."
    c. he regrets having not taken advantage of educational opportunities offered him.

2. When Rodriguez faces a fellow Mexican-American, he feels embarrassment, shame, and guilt

    a. because he takes no pride in his Mexican heritage.
    b. because he was not effective as a "Mexican-American representative."
    c. because he allows himself to continue to be numbered among the culturally disadvantaged.

3. Concerning his teaching career, Rodriguez's final decision is to

    a. reject all of the offers.
    b. accept the offer from Yale.
    c. go back to graduate school and pursue a career in another field.

4. In this essay, Rodriguez's thesis is that

    a. Mexican-Americans are skeptical of the so-called benefits of Affirmative Action.
    b. Affirmative Action often results in "reverse discrimination."
    c. Affirmative Action is essentially ineffective so long as the seriously disadvantaged are never reached.

5. Rodriguez makes the issue of Affirmative Action vivid

    a. by the use of the personal experience narrative.
    b. by just objectively stating his opinion about Affirmative Action in general.
    c. through a series of examples.

# CHAPTER 9: VOCABULARY QUIZ

## Richard Rodriguez, "None of This Is Fair"

NAME _____     DATE

Directions: Choose the correct definition for each of the following words.

### 1. BENEFICIARY

    a. one who loses
    b. one who evaluates
    c. one who profits

### 2. AVERTING

    a. keeping up
    b. turning away
    c. focusing or concentrating

### 3. WARY

    a. cautious
    b. serious
    c. conscious of

### 4. PLOY

    a. list of demands
    b. maneuver to gain an advantage
    c. desire for status

### 5. ASSERT

    a. to declare or defend
    b. to list defensively
    c. to amend or change

# CHAPTER 10: CONTENT QUIZ

## Jonathan Swift, "A Modest Proposal"

NAME _____     DATE

1. Who does Swift claim are "the principal breeders of the nation"?

    a. the young and irresponsible
    b. the Papists
    c. the alcoholics

2. Swift assumes that women who give themselves abortions do so to avoid

    a. the pain of birth.
    b. the shame of a birth out of wedlock.
    c. the expense of raising a child.

3. According to Swift's calculations, one male will be able to service how many females?

    a. 4
    b. 3
    c. 6
    d. 10

4. Which of the following is NOT part of Swift's modest proposal?

    a. cannibalism
    b. infanticide
    c. adoption

5. Why will Swift himself not benefit by such an idea?

    a. His children are all sons.
    b. His wife is past child-bearing.
    c. He lives in London, not in Ireland.

# CHAPTER 10: VOCABULARY QUIZ


Jonathan Swift, "A Modest Proposal"


NAME _____          DATE


Directions: Choose the correct definition for each of the following words.


## 1. MELANCHOLY

   a. happy
   b. sad
   c. frightening

## 2. DEPLORABLE

   a. regrettable
   b. unforgettable
   c. highly visible

## 3. PROLIFIC

   a. healthy and strong
   b. scarce
   c. productive or fruitful

## 4. IDOLATROUS

   a. sacred
   b. worshiping idols or false ideals
   c. ridiculous; absurd

## 5. TEMPERANCE

   a. moderation
   b. abstinence
   c. indulgence

CHAPTER 10: CONTENT QUIZ

Virginia Woolf, "The Death of the Moth"

NAME _____         DATE

1. Woolf says the moth was "little or nothing but . . . ?"

    a. an insect
    b. an annoyance
    c. dirty and germ-ridden
    d. life

2. Woolf believes the same energy that "inspires" animals outside also inspires the moth to

    a. give up his fight.
    b. flutter back and forth.
    c. search for food and water.

3. When Woolf writes that the moth drives through the "corridors" of her brain, she means

    a. it permeates her thoughts.
    b. it interrupts her work.
    c. it flies against her head.
    d. it flutters around her study.

4. What does Woolf use to try to roll the moth over?

    a. a pin
    b. a pencil
    c. a piece of paper
    d. a pair of tweezers

5. The moth's struggle against death fills Woolf with

    a. anger.
    b. sorrow.
    c. excitement.
    d. wonder.

# CHAPTER 10: VOCABULARY QUIZ

## Virginia Woolf, "The Death of the Moth"

NAME _____          DATE

Directions: Choose the correct definition for each of the following words.

1. ROOKS

   a. locusts
   b. birds
   c. butterflies

2. MEAGER

   a. abundant
   b. mealy or worm-filled
   c. scarce

3. DIMINUTIVE

   a. tiny
   b. furry
   c. swift or nimble

4. ROUSE

   a. to yawn
   b. to worry
   c. to stir up

5. AGITATED

   a. ceased moving
   b. moved violently
   c. moved slowly

# CHAPTER 10: CONTENT QUIZ

E. B. White, "Once More to the Lake"

NAME _____ DATE

1. What does White remember most about the lake?

    a. the other campers
    b. the early mornings
    c. the smell of the trees
    d. fishing

2. What is the one thing different about the waitresses when White goes to dinner at the farmhouse?

    a. They have a new style of uniform.
    b. They are older.
    c. They have clean hair.

3. According to White, what took a "cool nerve" to execute?

    a. swimming the length of the lake
    b. reversing the one-cylinder inboard motor
    c. asking a waitress out

4. To what does White compare the thunderstorm?

    a. strobe lights
    b. flashbulbs
    c. drums
    d. an earthquake

5. White feels a connection to the lake because

    a. he came here with his father.
    b. he once lived here.
    c. he owns the land.

# CHAPTER 10: VOCABULARY QUIZ

E. B. White, "Once More to the Lake"

NAME _____          DATE

Directions: Choose the correct definition for each of the following words.

1. INCESSANT

    a. intermittent; coming at intervals
    b. constant
    c. loud

2. PENSIVELY

    a. viciously
    b. easily
    c. thoughtfully

3. TRANSPOSITION

    a. the act of changing positions
    b. the act of carrying
    c. the act of transporting over time

4. PETULANT

    a. pleasing
    b. loud
    c. irritable

5. TRANQUIL

    a. quiet; peaceful
    b. asleep
    c. foreboding

# CHAPTER 10: CONTENT QUIZ

Joan Didion, "On Keeping a Notebook"

NAME _____          DATE

1. Why does Didion believe her daughter will never write?

    a. She has seen how difficult it is.
    b. She accepts life as it comes to her.
    c. She expresses little interest in writing.

2. Why does Didion not care if some of her entries are not "true"?

    a. She enjoys the fun of making up stories.
    b. The truth is too painful to recount.
    c. She writes things down as they felt to her, whether they are true or false.

3. Didion states that her notebook is ultimately about other people.

    a. true
    b. false

4. According to Didion, what is the common denominator to all that each of us sees?

    a. I
    b. God
    c. we

5. What was NOT the cause for Didion's dread in the supermarket?

    a. the human condition
    b. her desire for a $1000-a-month house
    c. her hangover

# CHAPTER 10: VOCABULARY QUIZ

Joan Didion, "On Keeping a Notebook"

NAME _____     DATE

Directions: Choose the correct definition for each of the following words.

1. VISCOUS

    a. sticky
    b. opaque
    c. clear

2. DIFFIDENT

    a. careless
    b. indifferent
    c. timid; shy

3. SELF-EFFACING

    a. arrogant; rude
    b. modest
    c. curious

4. COMPULSION

    a. trait
    b. urge
    c. means of moving

5. DISCERN

    a. to accept
    b. to confuse
    c. to perceive

# CHAPTER 10: CONTENT QUIZ

## Peter Singer, "The Singer Solution to World Poverty"

NAME _____          DATE

1. How much would it cost to help a sickly two-year-old become a healthy six-year-old?

    a. $3000
    b. $800–$1200 for each of the four years
    c. $200

2. In the middle of the essay, Singer draws an analogy between a fictional character and our own behavior concerning those in need. That example

    a. is drawn from a film with a woman named Dora and a young boy.
    b. involves a man who buys a valuable old automobile.
    c. is a young child who is in desperate need of food and medicine.

3. The need for financial aid is so great throughout the world that Singer advocates

    a. We shouldn't feel too guilty since the problem is too large for individuals to solve.
    b. As a nation we shouldn't accept the responsibilities unless other countries do too.
    c. We should just concentrate on those who are in need here within the United States.
    d. none of the above

4. The United States government contributes to overseas aid agencies

    a. more generously than any other nation in the world.
    b. and is among the largest contributors to such agencies.
    c. its "fair" share.
    d. none of the above

5. Singer argues that everyone in the United States should

    a. contribute 10% of their incomes to organizations that help the poor.
    b. donate all money they earn over and above $30,000 a year.
    c. stop eating in restaurants and donate that money to charity.

# CHAPTER 10: VOCABULARY QUIZ

Peter Singer, "The Singer Solution to World Poverty"

NAME _____     DATE

Directions: Choose the correct definition for each of the following words.

## 1. ACQUISITION

    a. a concession
    b. something that one buys or comes to have as one's own
    c. a religious trial or inquiry

## 2. GRAVELY

    a. fatally
    b. seriously
    c. quickly

## 3. PLAUSIBLE

    a. seemingly true or honest
    b. actual; genuine
    c. reluctantly; unsurely

## 4. FARCICAL

    a. plentiful
    b. serious
    c. ridiculous; absurd

## 5. DRASTIC

    a. comic
    b. extreme
    c. clever

# CHAPTER 1

## KEY TO CONTENT AND VOCABULARY QUIZZES

"The Name Is Mine"

| Content | Vocabulary |
|---|---|
| 1. c | 1. c |
| 2. b | 2. b |
| 3. a | 3. a |
| 4. b | 4. b |
| 5. b | 5. a |

"One of the Girls"

| Content | Vocabulary |
|---|---|
| 1. c | 1. a |
| 2. c | 2. a |
| 3. b | 3. a |
| 4. c | 4. b |
| 5. b | 5. c |

"Cut"

| Content | Vocabulary |
|---|---|
| 1. a | 1. c |
| 2. d | 2. a |
| 3. b | 3. b |
| 4. a | 4. b |
| 5. a | 5. a |

"Westbury Court"

| Content | Vocabulary |
|---|---|
| 1. c | 1. b |
| 2. a | 2. c |
| 3. b | 3. c |
| 4. d | 4. a |
| 5. c | 5. a |

"On Shooting an Elephant"

| Content | Vocabulary |
|---|---|
| 1. b | 1. a |
| 2. c | 2. c |
| 3. c | 3. b |
| 4. a | 4. c |
| 5. c | 5. a |

# CHAPTER 2

## KEY TO CONTENT AND VOCABULARY QUIZZES

"Salvation"

| Content | Vocabulary |
|---------|------------|
| 1. b | 1. c |
| 2. c | 2. a |
| 3. b | 3. a |
| 4. b | 4. b |
| 5. b | 5. c |

"Lockdown"

| Content | Vocabulary |
|---------|------------|
| 1. b | 1. a |
| 2. c | 2. c |
| 3. a | 3. a |
| 4. b | 4. c |
| 5. a | 5. c |

"Sister Monroe"

| Content | Vocabulary |
|---------|------------|
| 1. a | 1. a |
| 2. b | 2. b |
| 3. b | 3. b |
| 4. a | 4. b |
| 5. c | 5. c |

"Facing Famine"

| Content | Vocabulary |
|---------|------------|
| 1. a | 1. b |
| 2. c | 2. a |
| 3. b | 3. c |
| 4. b | 4. b |
| 5. b | 5. a |

"Marina"

| Content | Vocabulary |
|---------|------------|
| 1. b | 1. b |
| 2. c | 2. a |
| 3. b | 3. c |
| 4. a | 4. b |
| 5. b | 5. a |

# CHAPTER 3

## KEY TO CONTENT AND VOCABULARY QUIZZES

"A Pen by the Phone"

| Content | Vocabulary |
|---------|------------|
| 1. d | 1. a |
| 2. c | 2. b |
| 3. a | 3. c |
| 4. b | 4. c |
| 5. c | 5. b |

"The Inheritance of Tools"

| Content | Vocabulary |
|---------|------------|
| 1. b | 1. c |
| 2. a | 2. a |
| 3. b | 3. a |
| 4. c | 4. c |
| 5. c | 5. b |

"The Way to Rainy Mountain"

| Content | Vocabulary |
|---------|------------|
| 1. a | 1. a |
| 2. a | 2. c |
| 3. d | 3. b |
| 4. b | 4. a |
| 5. a | 5. a |

"Nameless, Tennessee"

| Content | Vocabulary |
|---------|------------|
| 1. c | 1. b |
| 2. b | 2. a |
| 3. a | 3. a |
| 4. b | 4. c |
| 5. c | 5. b |

"The Village Watchman"

| Content | Vocabulary |
|---------|------------|
| 1. b | 1. a |
| 2. b | 2. c |
| 3. c | 3. b |
| 4. b | 4. a |
| 5. b | 5. b |

# CHAPTER 4

## KEY TO CONTENT AND VOCABULARY QUIZZES

**"What's in Your Toothpaste?"**

| Content | Vocabulary |
|---------|-----------|
| 1. a | 1. a |
| 2. c | 2. a |
| 3. b | 3. a |
| 4. a | 4. b |
| 5. b | 5. c |

**"The Myth of the Latin Woman"**

| Content | Vocabulary |
|---------|-----------|
| 1. c | 1. b |
| 2. b | 2. c |
| 3. a | 3. a |
| 4. c | 4. a |
| 5. b | 5. b |

**"In Defense of Talk Shows"**

| Content | Vocabulary |
|---------|-----------|
| 1. b | 1. a |
| 2. c | 2. c |
| 3. b | 3. c |
| 4. a | 4. a |
| 5. a | 5. c |

**"The Value of Children"**

| Content | Vocabulary |
|---------|-----------|
| 1. c | 1. b |
| 2. a | 2. b |
| 3. b | 3. a |
| 4. b | 4. b |
| 5. b | 5. b |

**"How We Listen to Music"**

| Content | Vocabulary |
|---------|-----------|
| 1. c | 1. b |
| 2. a | 2. c |
| 3. c | 3. b |
| 4. b | 4. a |
| 5. d | 5. b |

**"What Are You Afraid of?"**

| Content | Vocabulary |
|---------|-----------|
| 1. c | 1. c |
| 2. a | 2. a |
| 3. c | 3. c |
| 4. b | 4. b |
| 5. b | 5. b |

+

# CHAPTER 5

## KEY TO CONTENT AND VOCABULARY QUIZZES

"Guavas"

| Content | Vocabulary |
|---------|------------|
| 1. b | 1. a |
| 2. c | 2. b |
| 3. d | 3. a |
| 4. a | 4. c |
| 5. b | 5. a |

"Neat People vs. Sloppy People"

| Content | Vocabulary |
|---------|------------|
| 1. b | 1. a |
| 2. d | 2. c |
| 3. a | 3. c |
| 4. c | 4. a |
| 5. b | 5. b |

"The Transaction"

| Content | Vocabulary |
|---------|------------|
| 1. c | 1. c |
| 2. a | 2. a |
| 3. a | 3. a |
| 4. a | 4. b |
| 5. b | 5. c |

"The Color of Love"

| Content | Vocabulary |
|---------|------------|
| 1. b | 1. b |
| 2. d | 2. a |
| 3. a | 3. a |
| 4. a | 4. a |
| 5. c | 5. c |

"Academic Selves"

| Content | Vocabulary |
|---------|------------|
| 1. c | 1. c |
| 2. d | 2. a |
| 3. b | 3. a |
| 4. c | 4. c |
| 5. b | 5. a |

"Virtual Love"

| Content | Vocabulary |
|---------|------------|
| 1. b | 1. a |
| 2. b | 2. b |
| 3. a | 3. c |
| 4. d | 4. a |
| 5. a | 5. b |

# CHAPTER 6

## KEY TO CONTENT AND VOCABULARY QUIZZES

"My Daily Dives"

| Content | Vocabulary |
|---------|------------|
| 1. d | 1. b |
| 2. a | 2. b |
| 3. c | 3. a |
| 4. b | 4. a |
| 5. b | 5. c |

"Into the Loop"

| Content | Vocabulary |
|---------|------------|
| 1. b | 1. c |
| 2. a | 2. a |
| 3. b | 3. a |
| 4. b | 4. b |
| 5. c | 5. b |

"Revision and Life"

| Content | Vocabulary |
|---------|------------|
| 1. b | 1. a |
| 2. b | 2. a |
| 3. b | 3. b |
| 4. c | 4. a |
| 5. a | 5. b |

"Stripped for Parts"

| Content | Vocabulary |
|---------|------------|
| 1. c | 1. b |
| 2. c | 2. a |
| 3. a | 3. a |
| 4. c | 4. b |
| 5. b | 5. c |

"Don't Just Stand There"

| Content | Vocabulary |
|---------|------------|
| 1. c | 1. a |
| 2. d | 2. a |
| 3. d | 3. c |
| 4. b | 4. b |
| 5. d | 5. a |

"The Culture of Martyrdom"

| Content | Vocabulary |
|---------|------------|
| 1. b | 1. c |
| 2. b | 2. a |
| 3. c | 3. c |
| 4. b | 4. b |
| 5. a | 5. a |

# CHAPTER 7

## KEY TO CONTENT AND VOCABULARY QUIZZES

"My Wood"

| Content | Vocabulary |
| --- | --- |
| 1. c | 1. b |
| 2. c | 2. a |
| 3. b | 3. b |
| 4. a | 4. a |
| 5. b | 5. b |

"Dreadlocked"

| Content | Vocabulary |
| --- | --- |
| 1. b | 1. b |
| 2. c | 2. a |
| 3. d | 3. a |
| 4. b | 4. a |
| 5. b | 5. c |

"The Origins of Anorexia"

| Content | Vocabulary |
| --- | --- |
| 1. c | 1. c |
| 2. a | 2. a |
| 3. a | 3. a |
| 4. e | 4. c |
| 5. d | 5. a |

"The Trouble with Fries"

| Content | Vocabulary |
| --- | --- |
| 1. c | 1. c |
| 2. c | 2. c |
| 3. b | 3. c |
| 4. c | 4. a |
| 5. c | 5. a |

"On Teenagers and Tattoos"

| Content | Vocabulary |
| --- | --- |
| 1. d | 1. b |
| 2. a | 2. c |
| 3. d | 3. a |
| 4. b | 4. c |
| 5. a | 5. b |

"Black Men and Public Space"

| Content | Vocabulary |
| --- | --- |
| 1. e | 1. a |
| 2. b | 2. b |
| 3. d | 3. a |
| 4. d | 4. c |
| 5. c | 5. a |

# CHAPTER 8

## KEY TO CONTENT AND VOCABULARY QUIZZES

"How Can Anyone"

| Content | Vocabulary |
|---------|------------|
| 1. b | 1. c |
| 2. c | 2. a |
| 3. d | 3. b |
| 4. a | 4. b |
| 5. b | 5. c |

"Mess"

| Content | Vocabulary |
|---------|------------|
| 1. c | 1. c |
| 2. a | 2. b |
| 3. b | 3. c |
| 4. c | 4. b |
| 5. a | 5. a |

"I Want a Wife"

| Content | Vocabulary |
|---------|------------|
| 1. c | 1. b |
| 2. c | 2. a |
| 3. b | 3. b |
| 4. b | 4. b |
| 5. a | 5. c |

"The Female Body"

| Content | Vocabulary |
|---------|------------|
| 1. c | 1. b |
| 2. d | 2. a |
| 3. b | 3. a |
| 4. b | 4. c |
| 5. c | 5. c |

"The People in Me"

| Content | Vocabulary |
|---------|------------|
| 1. a | 1. a |
| 2. c | 2. a |
| 3. c | 3. c |
| 4. c | 4. b |
| 5. a | 5. a |

"Mother Tongue"

| Content | Vocabulary |
|---------|------------|
| 1. d | 1. c |
| 2. c | 2. b |
| 3. c | 3. c |
| 4. d | 4. b |
| 5. c | 5. a |

# CHAPTER 9

## KEY TO CONTENT AND VOCABULARY QUIZZES

**"The Value of a College Degree"**

| Content | Vocabulary |
| --- | --- |
| 1. c | 1. c |
| 2. a | 2. a |
| 3. d | 3. b |
| 4. d | 4. c |
| 5. b | 5. b |

**"Memoirs of a Dead Man"**

| Content | Vocabulary |
| --- | --- |
| 1. c | 1. c |
| 2. a | 2. a |
| 3. b | 3. b |
| 4. d | 4. b |
| 5. b | 5. c |

**"The Case Against College"**

| Content | Vocabulary |
| --- | --- |
| 1. b | 1. a |
| 2. b | 2. b |
| 3. b | 3. c |
| 4. a | 4. c |
| 5. b | 5. c |

**"What Do Murderers Deserve?"**

| Content | Vocabulary |
| --- | --- |
| 1. c | 1. a |
| 2. b | 2. b |
| 3. a | 3. b |
| 4. c | 4. a |
| 5. b | 5. a |

**"When I Was Young"**

| Content | Vocabulary |
| --- | --- |
| 1. d | 1. b |
| 2. b | 2. c |
| 3. c | 3. a |
| 4. b | 4. c |
| 5. a | 5. b |

**"I Have a Dream"**

| Content | Vocabulary |
| --- | --- |
| 1. b | 1. b |
| 2. c | 2. c |
| 3. c | 3. b |
| 4. a | 4. a |
| 5. b | 5. a |

**"The Dangerous Myth"**

| Content | Vocabulary |
| --- | --- |
| 1. b | 1. c |
| 2. b | 2. c |
| 3. c | 3. b |
| 4. a | 4. d |
| 5. c | 5. c |

**"None of This Is Fair"**

| Content | Vocabulary |
| --- | --- |
| 1. b | 1. c |
| 2. c | 2. b |
| 3. a | 3. a |
| 4. c | 4. b |
| 5. a | 5. a |

# CHAPTER 10

## KEY TO CONTENT AND VOCABULARY QUIZZES

"A Modest Proposal"

| Content | Vocabulary |
|---------|-----------|
| 1. b | 1. b |
| 2. c | 2. a |
| 3. a | 3. c |
| 4. c | 4. b |
| 5. b | 5. a |

"On Keeping a Notebook"

| Content | Vocabulary |
|---------|-----------|
| 1. b | 1. a |
| 2. c | 2. c |
| 3. b | 3. b |
| 4. a | 4. b |
| 5. a | 5. c |

"The Death of the Moth"

| Content | Vocabulary |
|---------|-----------|
| 1. d | 1. b |
| 2. b | 2. c |
| 3. a | 3. a |
| 4. b | 4. c |
| 5. d | 5. b |

"The Singer Solution"

| Content | Vocabulary |
|---------|-----------|
| 1. a | 1. b |
| 2. b | 2. b |
| 3. d | 3. a |
| 4. d | 4. c |
| 5. b | 5. b |

"Once More to the Lake"

| Content | Vocabulary |
|---------|-----------|
| 1. b | 1. b |
| 2. c | 2. c |
| 3. b | 3. a |
| 4. c | 4. c |
| 5. a | 5. a |